Piper PA-38 Tomahawk
A Pilot's Guide

Piper PA-38 Tomahawk
A Pilot's Guide

Jeremy M Pratt

ISBN 1 874783 63 2

Airplan Flight Equipment

First Edition 1992
2nd Edition 2005

©Copyright 1992 Jeremy M Pratt and AFE Ltd.

Piper PA-38 Tomahawk
A Pilot's Guide
Jeremy M Pratt

ISBN 1 874783 63 2

Airplan Flight Equipment
1a Ringway Trading Estate
Shadowmoss Road
Manchester M22 5LH
Tel: 0161 499 0023
Fax: 0161 499 0298
www.afeonline.com

Contents

Authors Acknowledgments

I would like to thank all those whose knowledge, help and advice went into this book, in particular:

Air Nova

Airspeed Aviation

Wayne Barratt

Simon Booth

CAA Safety Promotion Section

CSE Aviation

Colourmatch

Adrian Dickinson

Steve Dickinson

David Hockings

Andy Holland

Phil Huntington

Wendy Mellor

Manchester School of Flying

Margaret Parkes

Paul Price

Ravenair

Neil Rigby

John Ross

Ian Sixsmith

Louise Southern

Robert Taylor, GDi studio

John Thorpe

Cover image courtesy of
Ravenair, Liverpool

Sarah, Kate and Miles

Jeremy M Pratt

August 1992

General Description

General Description

▶ The PA-38 Tomahawk

If a camel is a horse designed by a committee, then the Tomahawk is surely a trainer designed by instructors.

It was in the mid 1970's that Piper decided to build a true two place trainer – their first since the high-wing, tube and fabric PA-22 Colt built in the early 1960s. To this end an anonymous questionnaire was sent to 10,000 flying instructors, to determine the characteristics of their ideal trainer. The results make interesting reading, the top priorities included handling characteristics, performance, operating costs and cabin comfort; low noise level, the ability to spin and an easily accessible fuel selector also featured.

Deliveries of the PA-38 Tomahawk began in 1978. Even a cursory look over the aircraft revealed the design philosophies it incorporated. The high aspect ratio, constant cord wing gives the appearance of being somewhat longer than its 34ft span. The distinctive 'T-tail' – the tailplane perched at the top of the fin – helped give the aircraft its handling characteristics and was incidentally very fashionable on light aircraft designed around this time. The two door cabin offered 360° visibility, easy access and comfortable accommodation. Some parts of the aircraft are interchangeable ie main and nose wheels, elevators etc. The aircraft is powered by a Lycoming, 4 cylinder air cooled engine driving a fixed pitch propeller.

The strength and operation of the door hinging and latching system attracted early comment, as did the 'spring' elevator trim system; but perhaps most notably the stalling and spinning characteristics soon became a renowned feature of the Tomahawk.

In 1981 the Tomahawk II appeared. This model incorporated changes in response to several ADs (Airworthiness Directives) that had affected the original Tomahawk. In addition items such as sound proofing and door latching were improved, and inboard wing flow strips – fitted on the wing leading edge to make the stall more docile – were incorporated. The most obvious external difference between the two versions are the 6.00 x 6 wheels fitted as standard on the Tomahawk II.

Production of the PA-38 Tomahawk ceased in 1983, largely as a result of the 'product liability' situation that had made light aircraft manufacture uneconomic in the USA. Just under 2500 Tomahawks were produced in all, and it remains probably the last purpose designed civilian trainer to emerge from the USA.

▶ Model Numbers and Production Years

▶ The PA-38 Tomahawk

▶ The Airframe

▶ The Flying Controls

▶ The Undercarriage

▶ The Engine

▶ The Propeller

▶ The Ignition System

▶ The Oil System

▶ The Starter System

▶ The Fuel System

▶ The Carburettor

▶ The Electrical System

▶ The Stall Warner System

▶ The Lighting System

▶ The Suction System

▶ The Pitot-Static System

▶ The Heating and Ventilation System

▶ Seats and Harnesses

▶ Doors and Windows

TOMAHAWK

PILOT'S OPERATING HANDBOOK

AND

FAA APPROVED AIRPLANE FLIGHT MANUAL

SAMPLE ONLY

AIRPLANE SERIAL NO. 38--78A0737

AIRPLANE REGIST. NO. G-BGKY ~~Export~~

PA-38-112
REPORT: 2126 FAA APPROVED BY: *Ward Evans*

WARD EVANS
D.O.A. NO. SO-1
PIPER AIRCRAFT CORPORATION
VERO BEACH, FLORIDA

DATE OF APPROVAL:
JANUARY 20, 1978

FAA APPROVED IN NORMAL AND UTILITY CATEGORIES BASED ON FAR 23 AND FAR PART 21, SUBPART J. THIS HANDBOOK INCLUDES THE MATERIAL REQUIRED TO BE FURNISHED TO THE PILOT BY FAR 23 AND FAR PART 21, SUBPART J AND CONSTITUTES THE APPROVED AIRPLANE FLIGHT MANUAL AND MUST BE CARRIED IN THE AIRPLANE AT ALL TIMES.

"This is the flight manual which forms part of Certificate of Airworthiness Number 8772."

HANDBOOK PART NO. 761 658

The approved Pilot Operating Handbook/Flight Manual (illustrated above), as amended, is the only source of authoritative information. Each individual aircraft has its own individual POH/FM, in the interests of safety & good airmanship the pilot should be familiar with this document. This AFE Pilot Guide is not an authoritive document and should not be taken as such.

▶ Model Numbers and Production Years

PRODUCTION YEAR	MODEL	MODEL NAME
1978- 1981	PA-38-112	Tomahawk

PRODUCTION YEAR	MODEL	MODEL NAME
1981- 1982	PA-38-112	Tomahawk II

▶The Airframe

The PA-38 airframe is generally described as being of all metal construction. The primary structure is constructed of aluminium alloy, with the engine mount and undercarriage being made from steel. Some non-structural components such as the wing tips and undercarriage fairings are made from GRP.

The fuselage has a semi-monocoque structure, that is the vertical bulkheads and frames are joined by horizontal longerons and stringers which run the length of the fuselage. The metal skin is rivetted to the longerons and stringers, this arrangement is conventional for modern light aircraft and allows loads to be spread over the whole construction. At the rear of the fuselage the tail unit incorporates a high 'T-tail' – the tailplane being mounted at the top of the fin assembly. Underneath the rear fuselage a triangular combined tie down point and tail guard is fitted.

The wings are of cantilever design (unsupported by external struts or bracing) and have a 5° dihedral. A main 'I' bar spar extending through the entire length of each wing is joined in the centre of the fuselage with butt fittings. The spar is attached to each side of the fuselage and to the fuselage tunnel. An aft spar extends from wing tip to wing root and is joined to the fuselage side. On the upper surface of each wing a black walkway is marked, this is the only area of the wing to be walked on or stood on. Underneath each wing a metal ring is fitted to be used as a tie down point. In the same area there is also a cone shaped protrusion which is used as a jacking point for maintenance operations.

The 5° positive dihedral is evident head on

▶The Flying Controls

Dual flight controls are fitted as standard and link the cockpit controls to the control surfaces via cable and chain linkages. The controls are electrically bonded to the main airframe by means of a bonding strips and some surfaces have a static wick to dissipate static electricity to the atmosphere.

The AILERONS are of the differential type, moving upward through 26° and downward through 14°. A balance weight is incorporated at the outer end of each aileron inside the wing tip cavity.

The FLAPS are of the simple type, and manually operated from a lever between the cockpit seats and through a torque tube and push rods to the flap surfaces. Three positions can be selected, fully up (0°),1st stage (21°), and 2nd stage – fully down – (34°). On some PA-38s the flaps do not lock in the fully up position and so may droop or drop to the 1st stage when on the ground. The flap lever slot in the cockpit has a 'brush' designed to stop objects falling into the cavity below. Unfortunately there have been several incidents of pens, pencils etc falling through the brush and becoming tangled in the elevator cables. Some operators have fitted a perspex guard around the flap lever, however it is safest not to put any objects in this area at all.

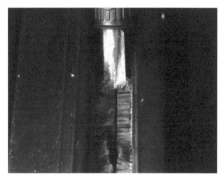

Flap lever slot with "brush"

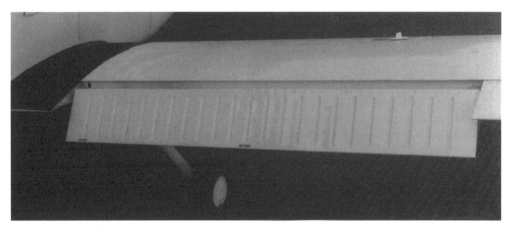

Flaps fully down (34°)

PA-38 Tomahawk tail unit

The **RUDDER** is operated from the rudder pedals (which are also linked to the steerable nose wheel) and can move through 29° either side of the neutral position. On the trailing edge of the control surface a ground adjustable trim tab is fitted. As the rudder is connected (via rods from the rudder pedals) to the nose wheel the control surface cannot be moved whilst the aircraft is stationary without exerting considerable force – this is not recommended.

The **ELEVATOR** is fitted to the tailplane on the 'T-tail'. The theory of the 'T-tail' arrangement on light aircraft is that the tailplane and elevator are mounted outside of the turbulent propeller slipstream and so give better handling characteristics. The control moves up through 34° and down through 20°, and incorporates a horn balance at the outer tip.

An adjustable **TRIM** system is incorporated into the elevator function. This control is of the spring type. Operation of the cockpit trim wheel acts on a spring which in turn exerts a bias on the elevator control circuit. It is probably fair to say that this system does not give as positive a trim as many other types, and in some situations it is possible to run out of 'nose up' trim. An indicator mounted next to the trim wheel shows the trim position set, and the control works in the natural sense, ie trimming the wheel forwards gives nose down trim and vice versa.

▶The Undercarriage

The Tomahawk undercarriage is fixed and of the tricycle type with a nose wheel rather than tailwheel.

The main gear has a 'leaf spring' steel undercarriage leg which attaches to the main spar, with a fairing where the leg joins the lower wing surface. Although almost fragile in appearance this arrangement is very strong – as you would expect on a training aircraft. However there have been some problems where the bolts used in the attachment have failed in normal usage, there is a service bulletin relevant to this problem. The main gear has a 10' track – the distance between the two main wheels.

The nose gear attaches to the engine mount and has an air/oil oleo strut to damp and absorb the normal operating loads. On the rear of the nose leg a torque link is fitted to maintain the correct alignment of the

Main wheel unit

Nose wheel assembly

nose wheel, its lower arm is fitted to the nose wheel fork and the upper arm to the oleo cylinder casing. The nose gear is steerable through direct linkage to the rudder pedals, the nose wheel has a range of movement of 30° either side of dead ahead.

The braking system consists of single disc brake assemblies fitted to the main undercarriage and operated by a hydraulic system. The brake lever in the cockpit operates a master cylinder located below and to the left of the throttle quadrant. When this control is pulled back braking is evenly applied to both main wheels, a small button on the brake lever allows it to be locked in the On position to act as a parking brake. To release the parking brake the lever is pulled back, and then pushed to its forward limit. The button automatically disengages. When optional toe brakes are fitted in addition, they are operated by depressing the upper half of the rudder pedal. In this system each toe brake has a separate brake cylinder above the pedal, and it is possible to operate the brakes differentially – to the port or starboard wheel. This system allows the aircraft to turn in a very tight circle, and it is possible to lock one main wheel with the use of some pedal force. Turning around a wheel in this fashion tends to 'scrub' the tyre and is generally discouraged. A brake fluid reservoir is fitted to the upper left forward face of the firewall (accessed via the port engine cowling). Here it can be inspected for fluid level and replenished if necessary

The undercarriage is fitted with 5.00 x 5 tyres as standard on the original Tomahawk. 6.00 x 6 tyres are fitted as standard on the Tomahawk II and were available as a option on the earlier aircraft, both tyres are of a four ply tube type.

Brake disc and brake unit (main wheel)

Brake fluid reservoir

▶The Engine

The Tomahawk is fitted with a Lycoming 0-235-L2C (Slick magnetos) or 0-235-L2A (Bendix magnetos), both versions are rated at 112 HP at 2600RPM.

The engine is a four cylinder unit, with cylinders horizontally opposed across the crankshaft. The cylinders are staggered so that each connecting rod has its own crankshaft throw, the cylinders and crankcase assembly are fashioned from aluminium alloy castings.

The engine is air cooled. Airflow enters the engine compartment at the front of the cowling, and is directed by baffles to flow over the whole engine. The cylinders feature deep cooling fins to aid cooling, the airflow leaves the engine compartment at the rear lower cowling underneath the engine compartment.

The engine is mounted on a steel tubular mounting which incorporates dynafocal insulators to reduce vibration, this mounting then attaches to the firewall. The mounting is designed to offset the engine centre line several degrees to the right (as seen from the cockpit), this offsets the thrust line to help counteract the slipstream effect which acts to the left.

Right hand view of Lycoming 0-235 engine

▶The Propeller

The propeller is an all metal, two bladed, fixed pitch design, turned by direct drive from the engine crankshaft, the propeller rotates clockwise as seen from the cockpit.

The pitch is 56" (determined at 75% of the diameter) and the diameter is 72", with a minimum allowable diameter of 70".

Slight offset of engine can be seen from head on

▶The Ignition System

The engine features a dual ignition system, fitted with two Slick or Bendix magnetos. The magnetos are small AC generators which are driven by the crankshaft rotation to provide a very high voltage to a distributor, which directs it via high voltage leads (or high tension leads) to the spark plugs. At the spark plug the current must cross a gap, in doing so a spark is produced which ignites the fuel/air mixture in the cylinder.

The magnetos are fitted at the rear of the engine, one each side of the engine centre line (hence Left and Right magnetos). The usual arrangement is for each magneto to fire one spark plug in each cylinder. Each cylinder has two spark plugs (top and bottom) for safety and efficiency. The leads that run from the magnetos to the spark plugs should be secure and there should be no splits or cracks in the plastic insulation covering the leads.

It is worth emphasising that the ignition system is totally independent of the aircraft electrical system, and once the engine is running it will operate regardless of the serviceability of the battery or alternator.

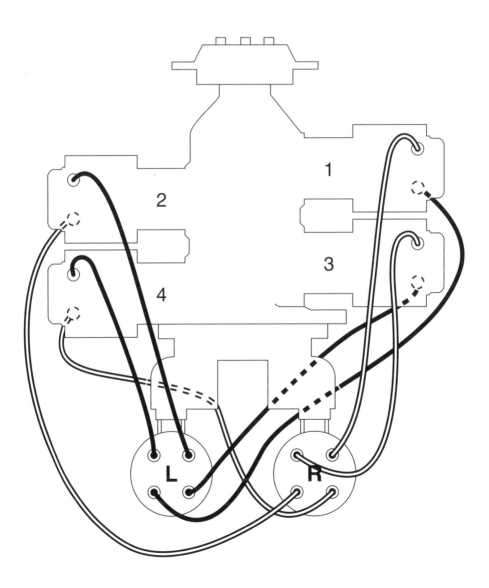

▶The Oil System

The oil system of the engine provides for lubrication, cooling, sealing, cleansing and protection against corrosion. The system is a wet – sump, pressure feed system. The oil sump is located under the engine, and oil is drawn from here by the engine driven oil pump, through a filter and into the oil gallery of the crankcase. When the oil has flowed around the engine it drains down to the sump by gravity. The oil filter is mounted at the upper rear of the engine and surrounded by a shroud, into which cooling air from the rear engine baffle is fed. There is also an oil pressure relief valve fitted, whose function is to maintain the correct operating pressure over a wide range of temperatures and RPM settings. Above a certain pressure this valve will open and allow oil to return to the sump rather than continuing into the lubricating system.

Oil contents can be checked on a dipstick on the right side of the engine. The dipstick is graduated in US quarts and measures the contents of the oil sump. When the engine has been running the oil will take up to 10 minutes to return to the sump, only then can a true reading be taken. When replacing the dipstick care should be taken not to overtighten the cap. To do so may make it exceptionally difficult to open the cap again, and it is quite possible to strip the thread on the cap or filler pipe.

The oil temperature and oil pressure gauges in the cockpit are electrically operated and linked to a sender unit in the engine.

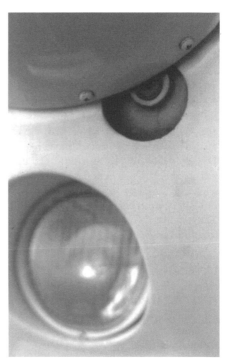

Oil filler pipe

▶The Starter System

The starter motor is housed at the lower front left side of the engine. It incorporates a geared cog that engages on to the teeth of the starter ring when the starter is operated. As the engine is turned an impulse coupling in the left magneto operates, this retards the spark and aids starting. When the engine fires and begins to rotate under its own power this impulse coupling ceases to operate and normal spark timing is resumed. When the key is released, allowing the key to return to the 'BOTH' position, the cog on the starter motor withdraws to be clear of the starter ring.

A STARTER WARNING LIGHT is fitted in the cockpit. This illuminates when the starter is operated to show that the starter motor is engaging the starter ring. When the key is released the light should go out. If the light remains on this means that the starter motor is still engaged with the starter ring. In this instance the starter motor will be turned by the engine, and serious damage may be caused to the aircraft electrical system. In this case the engine should be shut down without delay.

Just visible the starter motor unit above the landing light

Starter warning light next to clock (low voltage light below)

Underwing fuel strainer

Engine fuel strainer

▶The Fuel System

The Tomahawk has two aluminium fuel tanks, located in the inboard leading edge of each wing. From these tanks a fuel line runs through the wing and fuselage to the fuel selector valve. After this valve the fuel line runs through the firewall to a fuel strainer bowl mounted on the forward left face of the firewall. Beyond the strainer bowl a fuel line runs through the electric fuel pump and engine driven fuel pump to the carburettor. A separate line runs from the strainer bowl to the cockpit primer and from there to the engine primer nozzles.

Each tank has a TANK VENT, this is a forward facing pipe on the lower inboard surface of the wing which ensures that ambient pressure is maintained above the fuel in the fuel tank. Should this vent become blocked a vacuum may form in the tank as the fuel level lowers, and fuel flow to the engine may be interrupted.

There are three FUEL STRAINERS, one at the lower rear inboard edge of each tank, accessible from the inboard lower wing surface, and one from the fuel bowl, accessed at the lower left cowling. Fuel can only be drawn from the bowl if the cockpit fuel selector is in the Left or Right position.

The cockpit FUEL SELECTOR is a popular feature of the Tomahawk. The selector is centrally located on the power quadrant and easily accessible to each pilot. The selector can be used to feed the engine from either the Left or Right tank. To turn the fuel Off a spring loaded latch next to the bottom of the selector lever must first be depressed and then the lever rotated to the Off position. This operation can be a two handed operation, which does help prevent the accidental selection of the Off position.

In normal operation the fuel is drawn through the system by an engine driven FUEL PUMP. However should this pump fail the fuel supply to the carburettor will cease and the engine will stop. Therefore a second, electrical fuel pump is fitted, this pump is selected On or Off from a cockpit switch. Normally the electric fuel pump is used during take-off and landing, and when changing tanks. A fuel pressure gauge is fitted, reading from a sender between the engine driven fuel pump and the carburettor.

Cockpit fuel selector and throttle quadrant

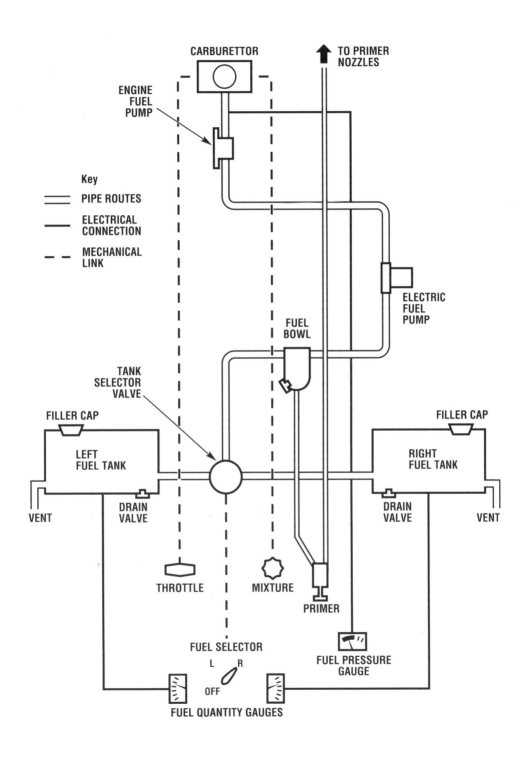

Key
PIPE ROUTES
ELECTRICAL CONNECTION
MECHANICAL LINK

CARBURETTOR

TO PRIMER NOZZLES

ENGINE FUEL PUMP

ELECTRIC FUEL PUMP

FUEL BOWL

TANK SELECTOR VALVE

FILLER CAP

FILLER CAP

LEFT FUEL TANK

RIGHT FUEL TANK

VENT

DRAIN VALVE

DRAIN VALVE

VENT

THROTTLE

MIXTURE

PRIMER

FUEL SELECTOR
L   R
OFF

FUEL PRESSURE GAUGE

FUEL QUANTITY GAUGES

▶The Carburettor

The carburettor mixes air with the fuel from the fuel system and supplies the fuel/air mix to the cylinders. The carburettor is located under the engine, and takes induction air from a scoop intake in the lower front cowling. This air is filtered and then fed into the carburettor air box. In this box a butterfly valve is used to allow either the induction air, or heated air, to be fed to the carburettor. Heated air comes from an unfiltered inlet inside the front cowling which then passes into a shroud around the exhaust which heats it before it reaches the carburettor. Hot or cold air is selected via the carburettor heat control in the cockpit, the use of this control and the subject of carburettor icing are fully discussed later in this book.

From the carburettor the fuel/air mix is carried through a 'centre zone induction manifold', that is the mix is carried through the engine oil sump which heats it to ensure more uniform vapourisation; it also aids in the cooling of the oil.

The primer control situated to the right of the throttle quadrant is an aid to starting. The control is unlocked by rotating the primer until a pin on the shaft aligns with the cut out in the collar. The control can then be pulled out, filling the pump with fuel from the fuel bowl. The primer is then pushed in, delivering fuel to the primer nozzles. When priming is complete the control should be pushed fully in with the pin aligned with the collar cut out, and then rotated about half a turn. As a check, attempt to pull the primer out, it should remain locked. It is important that the primer is fully locked, otherwise engine rough running may result.

The MIXTURE is controlled from the mixture lever located on the power quadrant in the cockpit which adjusts the fuel/air ratio in the carburettor. The use of this control is fully covered later in the book, however in the fully forward position it gives a RICH mixture, and if moved to the rearward ICO (Idle Cut Off) position the fuel supply is cut off and the engine stops.

The power quadrant has a vertical wheel on its lower centre edge. Movement of this 'friction' wheel adjusts the friction holding the throttle and mixture levers in position, and allows for them to be locked in a desired position. Generally this wheel is adjusted to leave the throttle and mixture with relatively loose and easy movement on the ground, but is tightened to hold the levers in position for take-off.

▶The Electrical System

The Tomahawk has a 14 volt, direct current electrical system. The alternator is mounted to the front lower right of the engine and is engine driven from a belt drive from a pulley directly behind the starter ring; the alternator is rated at 60 amps. A 12 volt, 25 ampere hour battery is located inside a vented box on the upper forward right side of the firewall.

The ALTERNATOR is the primary source of power to the electrical system in normal operations with the engine running. The alternator produces alternating current (AC) which is converted into direct current (DC) by diodes incorporated in the alternator housing which act as rectifiers. By their design, alternators require a small voltage (about 3 volts) to produce the electromagnetic field required inside the alternator. The significance of this is that if the battery is completely discharged (flat), the alternator will not be able to supply any power to the electrical system, even after the engine has been started by some other means (ie external power or hand swinging). Output from the alternator is controlled by a VOLTAGE REGULATOR which is mounted behind the right hand side of the instrument panel. An OVERVOLTAGE RELAY located next to the voltage regulator protects the system from possible damage due to an overvoltage condition. In the event of a voltage over approx 16.5v the relay opens and the alternator is isolated from the electrical system.

The primary purpose of the BATTERY is to provide power for engine starting, the initial excitation of the alternator and as a backup in the event of alternator failure. In normal operations with the engine running the alternator provides the power to the electrical system and charges the battery. A fully charged battery has a charging rate of about 2 amperes, in a partially discharged condition (ie just after engine start) the charging rate can be much higher than this. In the event of an alternator failure the battery provides ALL power to the electrical system. In theory a fully charged 25 ampere hour battery is capable of providing 25 amps for 1 hour, or 1 amp for 25 hours, or 12.5 amps for 2 hours etc. In practice the power available is governed by factors such as battery age and condition, load placed on it etc. In the case of an alternator failure while flying, the best advice is to reduce electrical load to the minimum consistent with safety, and plan to make a landing at the earliest opportunity.

The AMMETER, located in the engine instrument group to the right of the power quadrant, indicates in amperes the electrical load on the alternator. With the engine running and all electrical services turned off, the ammeter will indicate the charging rate of the battery. As services are switched on the ammeter will indicate the additional load of each item. In the case of night flight the maximum continuous load will be in the region of 30 amps. In the event of alternator failure the ammeter will indicate zero, and where fitted a red 'Low Voltage' warning light will illuminate.

The pilot controls the electrical system via the 'MASTER SWITCH' located on the left side of the instrument panel. This switch is a split rocker switch having two halves, labelled 'BAT' and 'ALT', and normally the switch is operated as one, both halves being used together. The 'BAT' half of the switch can be operated independently, so that all electrical power is being drawn from the battery only; however the 'ALT' side can only be turned on in conjunction with the 'BAT' half. Should an electrical problem occur the MASTER Switch can be used to reset the electrical system by turning it OFF for 2 seconds and then turning it ON again.

The aircraft may be fitted with an EXTERNAL POWER RECEPTACLE in the right hand fuselage behind the wing root, this can be used to connect external power for starting or operation of the aircraft electrical system. Before using external power it is imperative to check that the external power unit is of the correct voltage – otherwise SERIOUS DAMAGE COULD BE INFLICTED ON THE ELECTRICAL SYSTEM. Additionally it should be remembered that if the battery is totally flat (completely discharged), it will need to be removed and recharged or replaced before flight.

External power receptacle

The master switch (left) and electrical switches (right)

To use external power the following procedure should be adopted:

1   Check that MASTER SWITCH and all ELECTRICAL EQUIPMENT is OFF

2   Ensure that the RED lead of the jumper cable goes to POSITIVE terminal of the external
    power source and the BLACK lead to the NEGATIVE.

3   Insert the cable plug into the aircraft EXTERNAL POWER RECEPTACLE socket.

4   Turn the MASTER SWITCH ON, and proceed with normal starting procedure.

5   After engine start turn MASTER SWITCH and all ELECTRICAL EQUIPMENT OFF
    and remove the cable plug.

6   Turn the MASTER SWITCH ON, and check the ammeter. If no output is shown flight
    should not attempted.

The various electrically operated systems are protected by individual CIRCUIT BREAKERS, which are
located in a cluster on the right lower instrument panel. Should a problem (eg a short circuit) occur the
relevant circuit breaker may 'pop', and will be seen to be raised in relation to the other circuit breakers
(CBs). The correct procedure is to allow the CB to cool for say 2 minutes, then reset it and check the result.
If the CB pops again it should not be reset. The alternator field has a 60 ampere CB, and the voltage
regulator has a 5 ampere CB. All CBs show their rating and the components they protect.

Electrical fires are rare, but can be characterised by smoke in the cockpit and the distinctive smell of
burning insulation. The PA-38 has been involved in incidents where faults in the internal electrical system
have led to problems including smoke in the cockpit. In this case the problem may be solved by isolating
a circuit if a particular component is suspected (ie turning off the Nav lights if the smoke began after they
were switched on), or by turning off the master switch to shut down the electrical system. In either case it
is prudent to land at the earliest opportunity.

Apart from engine starting and the alternator field the electrical system supplies power to the following:

ALL internal and external lights.

ALL radios and intercom.

Turn Co-ordinator.

Stall Warner, Pitot Heater, Electric Fuel Pump.

Fuel Gauges, Oil Temperature Gauge and Oil Pressure Gauge.

The low voltage warning light (bottom left) and alternator warning light (upper right)

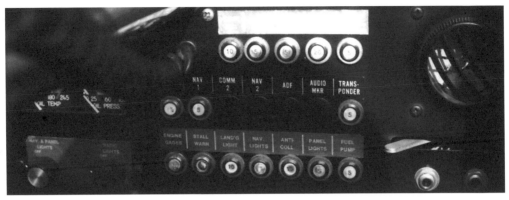

Circuit breaker panel

▶The Stall Warner System

An audible alarm located behind the instrument panel is electrically activated from a stall warning vane on the leading edge of the left wing. This vane moves up at angles of attack approaching the stall, and gives a warning at approx 5 to 10 knots above the stall speed. This vane can be checked before flight by gently moving the vane upwards with master switch on, the alarm should then be heard. With the master switch OFF, or with an electrical fault, the stall warner is inoperative.

Wing mounted stall warner vane

▶The Lighting System

The PA-38 may be equipped with a variety of optional internal and external lighting. A feature of most Tomahawks are the wingtip 'Strobe' lights which act as anti-collision lights. As a general rule the strobes are not used during taxying as they can dazzle and distract those nearby, they are however very effective in the air. If flying in cloud conditions or heavy precipitation it is recommended that they be turned off as the pilot may become spatially disorientated.

The wing tip navigation light and strobe light unit

The landing light is fitted in the lower front nose cowling, again it should be used with some discretion, not least because of the very short life of the lamp bulbs. Navigation lights are controlled from a switch on the lower right of the instrument panel which also controls the instrument panel lighting. This switch is of the rotatable rheostat type. When the switch is first turned on the navigation lights are illuminated at their set brilliance. The switch can be rotated to control the level of instrument panel lighting, the navigation lights remain

Cockpit lighting controls

at their set brightness until the switch is turned fully off. Next to this switch a similar switch controls just the radio panel lighting. There is also an overhead 'dome' light located in the cabin ceiling, this light is of a set brightness and has a on/off switch located to its side.

▶The Suction System

An engine driven vacuum pump is mounted to the upper rear face of the engine. This pump is fitted with a plastic shear drive, so that should the pump seize, the shear drive will fail and the engine will not be damaged. The air enters the suction system through a filter, passes through the air driven gyro instruments (and is measured by the suction gauge), flows through a vacuum regulator and into the vacuum pump, from which it is expelled through a short pipe.

Suction is used to drive the gyros in the Attitude Indicator (or Artificial Horizon) and Heading Indicator (or Direction Indicator). A suction gauge mounted on the instrument panel measures suction, for cruising RPMs and altitudes the reading should be 5.0 inches of mercury, +/-0.1 inches of mercury. At higher or lower settings the gyros may become unreliable. A lower suction over an extended period may indicate a faulty vacuum regulator, dirty screens or a system leak. If the vacuum pump fails or a line collapses the suction gauge reading will fall to zero, and the Attitude Indicator and Heading Indicator will become unreliable over a period of some minutes as the gyros run down losing RPM. The real danger here is that the effect is gradual and may not be noticed by the pilot for some time.

The engine driven suction pump

▶The Pitot-Static System

The pitot-static system supplies static pressure to the Vertical Speed Indicator (VSI) and Altimeter, and static and pitot pressure to the Air Speed Indicator (ASI).

Pitot pressure comes from a PITOT HEAD which is located under the left wing. Static pressure comes from two STATIC VENTS located on the rear fuselage (one each side). The use of two static vents is designed to help alleviate position error and manoeuvre induced error on the pressure instruments.

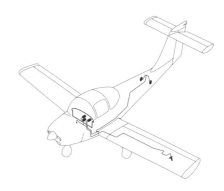

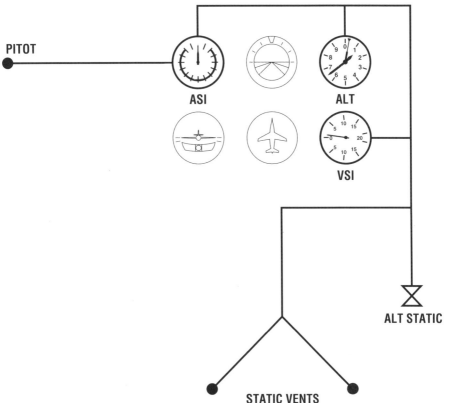

No checking system is incorporated in the system, and instrument indications in the event of a leak or blockage are outside of the scope of this book, however both the pitot head and the static vents have back up systems.

As an option the pitot head has a heating element which is activated by a switch in the electrical rocker switch group in front of the pilot, labelled 'PITOT HEAT'. Pitot heat can prevent blockage of the pitot head in heavy rain or icing, this aside, it must be remembered that the PA-38 IS NOT CLEARED FOR FLIGHT INTO KNOWN ICING CONDITIONS.

An alternate static source is fitted in the cockpit to be used in the case of failure or blockage of the normal static vents.

The pitot head

The external static vents should be checked before flight to ensure that they are clear and unobstructed. A similar check is carried out on the pitot head, which may be protected on the ground with a removable pitot cover. It is important not to blow into either pitot or static vents, doing so can result in damage to the pressure instruments.

The left fuselage static vent

▶The Heating and Ventilation System

Cabin heating is supplied via a shroud around the engine exhaust system. This allows air from inside the cowling to be warmed by the exhaust pipes, it can then be directed to outlets in the footwells (cabin heat) or at the lower windscreen (defrost) by two levers mounted on the lower left instrument panel. The system is very effective once the engine is warm, although its use is governed by a couple of safety factors.

Firstly the heating system effectively opens a path through the firewall between the engine compartment and the cockpit. For this reason the cabin heat and defrost are selected OFF before engine start, or if fire is suspected in the engine compartment.

Secondly with a system of this type there is a danger of Carbon Monoxide (CO) being introduced into the cabin. Carbon Monoxide is a gas produced as a by product of the combustion process. It is colourless, odourless and tasteless, but its effects are potentially fatal; the dangers of Carbon Monoxide poisoning are

External air vent

widely publicised. A generally accepted practice is to shut off the heating system if engine fumes (which may contain CO) are thought to be entering the cockpit. The danger arises if a crack or split is present in the exhaust system inside the heating shroud allowing carbon monoxide to enter the heating system.

The ventilation system consists of two cockpit vents, to the extreme right and left of the instrument panel, which control fresh air from their respective external air intakes located in the forward fuselage sides. The cockpit vents can be adjusted to control the direction and force of the fresh air into the cockpit. When the heating system is in use it is recommended that the fresh air vents be operated to give a comfortable temperature mix. Doing so will help to combat the possible danger of carbon monoxide poisoning, and on a more mundane level will stop the cabin becoming 'stuffy' and possibly inducing drowsiness in the pilot.

▶Seats and Harnesses

The seats are adjustable fore and aft. The handle which unlocks the seat position is located on the centre of the seat frame below the forward edge of the seat cushion. This handle is raised (by turning 1/4 turn) and then the seat can be moved fore and aft, a recess is provided in the upper part of the instrument coaming in front of each pilot to give the necessary grip for the free hand. The control column, engine levers or coaming overhang should NOT be used as an alternative handgrip. The seat tracks are inclined so that as the seat is moved forward the seating level is raised, and vice versa. When the desired position is reached the handle is returned to the vertically down position, and the pilot should check that the seat is positively locked in position. Generally entry to and exit from the seats is easiest with the seats in the rearmost position. When the seats are unoccupied the seat backs can be tilted forward to allow access to the baggage compartment.

Harness design may vary between different aircraft. In addition to the lap strap, shoulder straps of some description should be fitted and their use should be considered mandatory, as upper torso restraint has been shown to be a major factor in accident survivability. Final adjustment of the harness should be done when the seat is in the desired location.

The baggage area behind the seats is fitted with diagonal restraint straps for the securing of items placed in this area. Maximum baggage to be carried in this area is 100lbs (45Kg), evenly distributed so as not to give a loading in excess of 25lbs (11Kg) per sq ft. Attention should be drawn to the weight and balance implications of weight in this area, it also must be remembered that for some manoeuvres the carriage of baggage is prohibited.

▶ Doors And Windows

The Tomahawk has a door each side of the cabin to allow for easy access to the cabin via the wing walkways, these doors are fitted with two internal latches. The main door latch is located on the lower window sill. To lock this latch the lever is moved forward to the horizontal position, to unlatch, the lever is moved up and back to slightly past the vertical position. There is also an upper latch to hold the top edge of each door securely to the airframe. Unfortunately this latch is nowhere as simple or positive in operation as the main latch. The lever must first be rotated to be pointing forward, it is then rotated clockwise to be pointing aft, during this rotation the two top door hooks should engage on a loop in each door top. Operation of this upper latch is characterised by the amount of force often needed to bring the lever to the aft pointing position. If the lever appears very slack in rotating chances are that the doors have not latched. It is also possible that one door may latch and not the other. Frequently the plastic trim around the upper latch has been removed by operators to check door engagement, and to facilitate door latching.

Although it is important for the doors to be properly latched for flight, the consequences of partial door opening in flight are usually not serious. Where accidents do occur after a door opening in-flight, they are often caused by pilot distraction rather than as a direct result of the open door.

When entering and leaving the cabin, the top of the doors should not be used as a hand grip to support body weight, as damage to the door and door hinges may result.

An inward opening 'STORM WINDOW' is fitted to the left hand window. This window can be opened in flight where visibility through the windscreen has been impaired, or to aid ventilation.

The aircraft design and window area gives the Tomahawk exceptionally good all-round visibility. However this visibility can be degraded by oil smears, insects and other matter accumulating on the windows. For window cleaning a soft cloth and warm soapy water is recommended, to remove oil and grease a cloth soaked in kerosene can be used. The use of petrol, alcohol, thinners and window cleaner sprays is not recommended.

The roof mounted door locking handle

The door lever and storm (DV) window

Limitations

Limitations

▶ PA-38 Tomahawk Dimensions

▶ The 'V' Airspeed Code

▶ Airspeed Limitations PA38 Tomahawk

▶ Airspeed Indicator Markings

▶ Maximum Demonstrated Crosswind Component

▶ Airframe Limitations

▶ Flight Load Factors

▶ Performance Limitations

▶ Engine Limitations

▶ Oil System Limitations

▶ Fuel System

▶ Miscellaneous Limitations

▶ Oil Grades

▶ Fuel Grades

▶PA-38 Tomahawk Dimensions

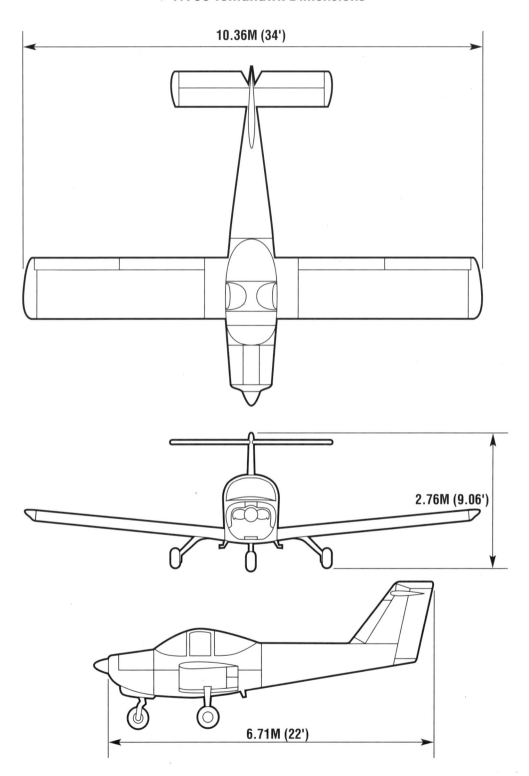

▶The 'V' Airspeed Code

VS0 (Bottom of white arc) Stalling speed with full flap.

VS1 (Bottom of green arc) Stalling speed 0 flap.

VFE (Top of white arc) Maximum airspeed with flaps extended. Do not extend flaps above this speed, or fly faster than this speed with any flap extended.

VA Design manoeuvring speed. Do not make full or abrupt control movements when flying faster than this speed. Design manoeuvring speed should not be exceeded when flying in turbulent conditions.

VNO (Top of green arc) Maximum structural cruising speed. Do not exceed this speed except in smooth air conditions.

VNE (Red line) Never exceed speed. Do not exceed this airspeed under any circumstances.

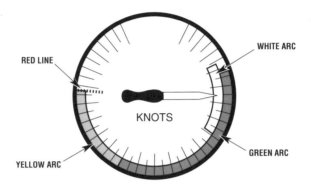

▶Airspeed Limitations – PA-38 Tomahawk

(all quoted speeds are INDICATED airspeed – IAS)

	KNOTS	MPH	KPH
VNE	138	159	255
VNO	110	126	204
VA (at 1670 lb)	103	118	191
VA (at 1277 lb)	90	103	167
VFE	89	102	165
Stalling Speed clean (with outboard flow strips only)	48	55	89
Stalling Speed clean (with inboard and outboard strips)	52	60	96
Stalling Speed Full Flap (with outboard flow strips only)	47	54	87
Stalling Speed Full Flap (with inboard and outboard strips)	49	56	91

▶ Airspeed Indicator Markings

	KNOTS	MPH	KPH
RED LINE (Never Exceed)	138	159	255
YELLOW ARC (Caution range)	110-138	126-159	204-255
GREEN ARC(Normal operating range – outboard flow strips	48-110	55-126	89-204
GREEN ARC (Normal operating range) – outboard & inboard strips	52-110	60-126	96-204
WHITE ARC (Flap extended range – outboard flow strips	47-89	54-102	87-165
WHITE ARC (Flap extended range) – outboard & inboard strips	49-89	56-102	91-165

▶ Maximum Demonstrated Crosswind Component

15 Knots

▶ Airframe Limitations

WEIGHTS	NORMAL		UTILITY	
	lbs	Kg	lbs	Kg
Maximum Take-off Weight	1670	757	1670	757
Maximum Landing Weight	1670	757	1670	757
Maximum Baggage Weight	100	45	0	0

▶ Flight Load Factors

Max Positive load factor	NORMAL	UTILITY
FLAPS UP	3.8G	4.4G
FLAPS DOWN	2.0G	2.0G

Max Negative load factor: NO INVERTED MANOEUVRES PERMITTED

▶ Performance Limitations

Service Ceiling	12000ft
Absolute Ceiling	14000ft

▶ Engine Limitations

Maximum RPM	2600

▶ Oil System Limitations

	Oil Temperature	Instrument Marking
Normal operating range	75-245°F	Green Arc
Maximum	245°F	Red Line

	Oil Pressure	Instrument Marking
Normal operating range	60-90psi	Green Arc
Minimum	15psi	Red Line
Maximum	100psi	Red Line
Caution range-idle	15-60psi	Yellow Arc
Caution range-warm up	90-100psi	Yellow Arc

▶ Oil Quantity

Note: dipstick is marked in US quarts

	US quart	Litre
Capacity	6	5.68
Minimum safe quantity	2 (+1 per hour planned flight)	1.89

▶ Fuel System

Fuel Quantity *Note: cockpit fuel gauges are marked in US gallons*

	US Gal	Imp Gal	Litre
Capacity	32	26.50	121
Unuseable Fuel	2	1.6	8
Usable Fuel	30	25	113

Fuel Pressure		Gauge Indication
Maximum	8.0psi	Red Line
Minimum	0.5psi	Red Line
Normal operating range	0.5-8.0psi	Green Arc

▶ Miscellaneous Limitations

Nose Wheel Tyre Pressure	26 PSI	1.8 Bar (5.00 x 5)	**Tomahawk I**
Main Wheel Tyre Pressure	26 PSI	1.8 Bar (5.00 x 5)	
Nose Wheel Tyre Pressure	30 PSI	2.1 Bar (6.00 x 6)	**Tomahawk II**
Main Wheel Tyre Pressure	30 PSI	2.1 Bar (6.00 x 6)	

▶Oil Grades

Lycoming approve lubricating oil for the engine that conforms to specification MIL-L-6082 (straight mineral type) and specification MIL-L-22851 (ashless dispersant type).

Straight mineral type – known mostly as straight oil – is usually only used when the engine is new, or after maintenance work on the engine. Straight oil grades are known by their number – ie 80, 100.

Ashless dispersant oils are more commonly used in service. These oil grades carry the prefix 'W', ie W80, W100. Ashless dispersant type – 'W' oil – must not be used where the engine is operating on straight oil, nor can 'W' oil be added to straight mineral oil. It is therefore very important to check which type of oil is currently being used in the engine, and be sure only to add the same type.

Both types of oil are available in different grades, used according to the average ground air temperature. The recommended grades are set out as SAE numbers, but available in commercial grade numbers – which are different! Thankfully the situation is more simple than it appears, to get the commercial grade, double the SAE number, ie SAE 50 = commercial grade 100 (or W100). The table below shows the recommended grades for various temperature bands.

AVERAGE AIR TEMPERATURE	MIL-L-6082 Straight mineral	COMMERCIAL GRADE
Above 60°F/16°C	SAE 50	100
30°F/-1°C – 90°F/32°C	SAE 40	80
0°F/-18°C – 70°F/21°C	SAE 30	65
Below 10°F/-12°C	SAE 20	55

AVERAGE AIR TEMPERATURE	MIL-L-22851 Ashless Dispersant	COMMERCIAL GRADE
Above 60°F/16°C	SAE 50 or SAE 40	W100 or W80
30°F/-1°C – 90°F/32°C	SAE 40	W80
0°F/-18°C – 70°F/21°C	SAE 30 or SAE 40	W65 or W80
Below 10°F/-12°C	SAE 30	W65

▶ Fuel Grades

The PA-38 Tomahawk is certified for use with 100LL fuels.

The table below shows the recommended fuel grades. It is wise to pay attention when your aircraft is being refuelled, especially if at an airfield new to you. More than one pilot has found out to their cost that piston engines designed for AVGAS do not run very well on AVTUR (Jet A-1). To help guard against this eventuality AVGAS fuelling points carry a RED sticker, and AVTUR fuelling points a BLACK sticker.

APPROVED FUEL GRADES

100LL

100L

100

Handling the Piper PA-38 Tomahawk

Handling the Piper PA-38 Tomahawk

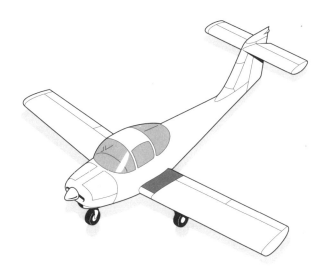

▶ Engine Starting

▶ Starting with a Suspected Flooded Engine

▶ Starting in Cold Ambient Conditions (Below 0°C)

▶ Taxying

▶ Power & Pre-Take-Off Checks

▶ Take-Off

▶ Climbing

▶ Cruising Flight

▶ Stalling

▶ Spins

▶ Descent

▶ Landing

▶ Parking and Tie Down

►Engine Starting

Starting of the Tomahawk is straightforward, but the ambient conditions and engine temperature are the prime factors to be considered. A cold engine will require between 2 and 4 primes, a hot engine should not require any priming at all. The throttle is set to 1/4" open (that is 1/4" in), with the mixture rich and fuel set to the tank with the lowest contents (unless of course that tank is empty). The Tomahawk is NOT fitted with an accelerator pump, and so 'pumping' the throttle during starting will serve no purpose (other than to cause an excessively lean mixture).

Cranking of the starter should be limited to 30 seconds at a time due to the danger of the starter motor overheating. After a prolonged period of engine cranking without a successful start the starter should be allowed a few minutes to cool before a further attempt is made. The starter should not be operated after engine start as damage to the starter may result. The starter warning light should go out after engine start, if it remains lit the engine should be shut down without delay.

After start the oil pressure should register within 30 seconds. Should the oil pressure not register the engine should be shut down without delay. Readings on the suction gauge and ammeter are also usually checked after engine start.

►Starting With a Suspected Flooded Engine

An overprimed (flooded) engine will be indicated by weak intermittent firing, and puffs of black smoke from the exhaust during the attempted start. If it is suspected that the engine is overprimed (flooded) the throttle should be opened fully and the mixture moved to idle cut off. If the engine starts the throttle should be retarded to the normal position and the mixture moved to fully rich.

►Starting In Cold Ambient Conditions (below 0°C)

Failure to start due to an underprimed engine is more likely to occur in cold conditions with a cold engine. An underprimed engine will not fire at all, and additional priming is necessary. Starting in cold temperatures will be more difficult due to a number of factors. The oil will be more viscous, the battery may lose up to half of its capacity and the fuel will not vapourise readily. A greater number of primes will be required, external power may be needed to supplement the aircraft battery, and pre-heat may be necessary in very low temperatures.

►Taxying

In the first few feet of taxying a brake check is normally carried out, followed by steering and differential brake checks in due course. It is common practice to check the hand operated brake lever in addition to the toe brakes. The direct link, via steering rods, from the rudder pedals to the nose wheel makes the Tomahawk easy to steer accurately. Use of differential brake can give a very small turning circle, so increased power is often required when using prolonged differential braking. When taxying with a crosswind 'opposite rudder' will be required, up to full deflection. i.e. with a crosswind from the left, up to full right rudder may be required as the aircraft tries to 'weathercock' into wind. In this situation differential braking may also be required.

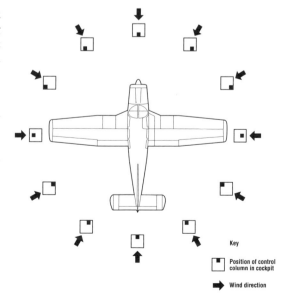

Key

■ Position of control column in cockpit

➡ Wind direction

The chart shows recommended control column positions when taxying with the prevailing wind from the directions shown.

Speed control is important, especially when taxying over rough surfaces or in strong wind conditions. When slowing the aircraft the throttle should always be closed firstly, and then the brakes evenly applied to slow the aircraft.

▶ Power And Pre-take-off Checks

The aircraft is usually positioned into wind to aid engine cooling, and before the power checks start the oil temperature should be in the green arc.

The engine is generally run up to 1800-2000RPM, with the fuel tank with the greatest contents selected (the same tank should be used for take-off). At this RPM the carburettor heat is checked, and a small drop in RPM should be noted. The subject of carb icing is covered more fully later, however an important point to note is that the inlet for the 'hot' air is unfiltered, and so dust, grass etc may well enter the engine when 'hot' air is selected, leading to increased engine wear. For this reason the use of carb heat should be kept to the minimum necessary whilst on the ground.

The magnetos are checked individually, with no more than 3 seconds on each magneto being recommended to avoid spark plug fouling. A small drop in RPM is the norm and shows that the ignition system is functioning properly. No RPM drop at all when operating on one magneto may well indicate a malfunction in the ignition system, and the possibility that one or both magnetos are staying 'live'. An excessive drop in RPM when operating on one magneto, especially when accompanied by rough running, may indicate fouled spark plugs or a faulty magneto. If fouled plugs are suspected it may be possible to clear the problem. The engine is set to about 2000RPM with magnetos on 'BOTH', and the mixture leaned to give the 'peak' RPM. This should be held for about 10 seconds, then the mixture is returned to fully rich and the magnetos can be re-checked.

> **WARNING:** Excessive power setting and over lean mixture settings should be avoided during this procedure. If the problem does not clear the aircraft should be considered unserviceable.

The engine gauges are checked at 1800-2000RPM for normal indications, together with the suction gauge and ammeter.

▶ Take-Off

Normally take-off is made with the mixture in the fully RICH position. At high elevation airfields (above say 3000' AMSL) it may be necessary to lean the mixture before take-off to give max power.

For all take offs care must be taken to ensure that the feet remain clear of the toe brakes, this is best done by keeping the heels on the floor. Inadvertent pressure on the toe brakes can significantly slow the aircraft during the take-off run, and lead to directional control difficulties.

At the start of the take-off run (as at all other times), the throttle should be opened smoothly and progressively, rapid opening of the throttle should be specifically avoided. The normal rotate speed is 53 knots, with a climb speed of 70 knots dependent on conditions and operator procedures. In crosswind conditions the Tomahawk can prove a handful, particularly in directional control as the speed increases prior to rotate. The recommended rotate speed in a crosswind is 60 Knots. For 'short field' take offs the use of 1 stage of flap (21°) is common practice.

On rough surfaces particularly, it is important to protect the nose wheel by keeping weight off it during the take-off run, although 'over-rotating' should be avoided as this will lengthen the take-off run (and ruin the view ahead!).

▶ Climbing

An airspeed in the region of 70 Knots will give the best rate of climb after take-off. The best angle of climb (the best increase in height for the shortest distance travelled over the ground) is obtained at 61 Knots when 1 stage of flap is lowered. During climbing it is important to monitor the engine gauges, as the engine is operating at a high power setting but with a reduced cooling airflow compared to cruising flight. Lookout ahead is impaired by the high nose attitude, and it is good airmanship to 'weave' the nose periodically during the climb to visually check the area ahead.

▶ Cruising Flight

Cruising is normally done with a power setting of 55-75%. Typically a setting of about 2200RPM will give an indicated airspeed of around 90 knots.

Engine rough running can be caused by a number of factors, unfortunately the majority of engine failures in light aircraft are caused by pilot error. After carburettor icing, fuel exhaustion (running out of fuel) or fuel starvation (ie fuel on-board but not reaching the engine) are common causes of engine failure. Having sufficient fuel on board to complete the flight is a point of basic airmanship, and can be accomplished by proper flight planning and thorough pre-flight checks. In flight, keeping the fuel tanks in balance and monitoring the fuel system is a function of the cruise checks. In the Tomahawk fuel starvation may occur if the engine driven fuel pump fails, in this instance the use of the electric fuel pump should restore the fuel supply to the engine and allow for a diversion to be made.

Regular monitoring of the engine instruments may forewarn of an impending problem. HIGH OIL TEMPERATURE may indicate a faulty gauge, if not accompanied by a corresponding drop in oil pressure. As with most instances the action to be taken will depend on the pilots judgment of the situation at the time. As general guidance a diversion to a suitable airfield, whilst remaining alert to the possibility of a sudden engine failure would make a reasonable course of action. **Where high oil temperature is accompanied by a low oil pressure, engine failure may very well be imminent, and the pilot should act accordingly.** That said such a situation might occur during a prolonged slow climb in hot conditions. In this instance increasing the airspeed to provide more cooling, and reducing power, if possible, may restore oil temperature to normal. In the event of a LOW OIL PRESSURE reading, accompanied by a normal oil temperature reading, gauge failure may be the culprit, and the pilot can consider actions similar to those for an oil temperature gauge failure.

▶ Stalling

> **Note:** *The information in this section is no substitute for flying instruction under the guidance of a flying instructor familiar with the aircraft and its characteristics.*

The Tomahawk is conventional in its stalling behaviour. The stall warning horn activates at 5 to 10 knots above the stall airspeed. Because this horn is electrically operated, the stall warning system is inoperative with the master switch off, or with a faulty electrical system. The actual stall speed can be affected by many factors including the aircraft weight and centre of gravity position. The use of power will lower the stalling speed, whilst turning flight raises the stall speed. The use of flaps, power or turning flight considerably increases the chances of a wing drop at the stall. When practicing stalls the possibility of a wing drop can be reduced by keeping the aircraft in balance during the approach to the stall. Typical height loss for a full stall with a conventional recovery (using power) is about 200'. Airframe buffeting (mostly of the tail surfaces) precedes the stall and is a feature of the Tomahawk.

The 1 Knot differential between zero flap and full flap stalling speeds (for models with outboard flow strips only) give a good indication of the overall lack of effectiveness of the flaps.

Stalling in the Tomahawk is usually achieved with the control wheel held fully aft. There have been instances where in this position the control shaft can be lifted vertically, binding the control wheel and preventing any forward movement. A modification is available to prevent this happening, however care should be taken when the control wheel is being held fully aft.

▶Spins

> **Note:** *The information in this section is no substitute for flying instruction under the guidance of a flying instructor familiar with the aircraft and its characteristics.*

The Tomahawk is approved for intentional spinning when operating in the utility category, however -

INTENTIONAL SPINS WITH FLAPS EXTENDED ARE PROHIBITED.

The Tomahawk spin has been the centre of much comment and discussion since the aircraft entered service. This may be because the aircraft does exhibit what can be described as 'classic' spin and spin recovery characteristics, which perhaps are not so apparent on other contemporary training aircraft.

As with stalling several factors can effect the behaviour of the aircraft in the spin. It is quite possible to devote a whole book just to this subject, and it is not the intention here to write a text book on spinning, however some points are worthy of mention. The weight of the aircraft (and particularly the c.g. position) has a noticeable effect on the spin. High weights tend to extend the spin recovery due to the increase in inertia. The position of the ailerons is important in spinning. The ailerons should be held NEUTRAL throughout the spin and recovery.

Piper recommend that the aircraft should be trimmed for a glide at 75 knots, and that the spin is entered power off at the stall. The spin is fairly standard, it is the spin recovery that must be carefully considered. As normal full rudder is applied opposite to the spin direction, the control wheel is moved rapidly forward WITHOUT DELAY. It must be appreciated that in the Tomahawk the control wheel will probably need to be FULLY FORWARD (in other words full down elevator) to achieve spin recovery. The immediate result may be that the spin steepens and speeds up, this sometimes leads the pilot to think that the incorrect actions have been taken – this is not the case. There is usually a delay of between ½ and 1½ turns before the spin stops, during this time the full and proper recovery actions must be maintained. The recovery occurs with a steep nose down attitude, for this reason it is acceptable to relax the forward pressure on the control wheel ONCE THE AIRCRAFT HAS STOPPED SPINNING. The rudder is then centred and the aircraft is recovered from the dive. Due to the steep nose down attitude in the recovery it is important to quickly centralise the rudder before the speed builds up above VA (103 Knots). The dive out following spin recovery is characterised by the high speed reached and height lost.

To summarise, the spin recovery is as follows:

- ■ Check ailerons neutral and throttle closed
- ■ Apply and maintain full opposite rudder (opposite to the direction of spin)
- ■ Move the control wheel immediately forward and maintain until the stall is broken and the spin stops. When the spin stops, it is permissible to relax the forward pressure on the control wheel to reduce the nose down attitude in the dive out.
- ■ When spin stops centralise the rudder quickly, and recover from the ensuing dive.

▶Descent

The descent may be powered or glide, for the glide a speed of 70 knots is standard. Where flaps are used the rate of descent increases, the initial lowering of flap leads to a slight nose down pitching and reduced airspeed. The low power settings usually used during the descent, and a possible prolonged descent into warmer air, provide ideal conditions for carburettor icing. Full carburettor heat should be used where necessary, and in a glide descent power should be added for short periods throughout the descent to help prevent plug fouling, rapid cylinder cooling and of course carb. icing.

▶ Landing

For the approach to landing the mixture should be fully RICH (unless landing at a very high elevation airfield), the electric fuel pump should be on and the fullest fuel tank selected. The Tomahawk is almost universally described as being an easy aircraft to land, the elevator being particularly effective right through the landing. This does not prevent the Tomahawk (as with many other light aircraft) appearing year after year in landing accident reports. It is rare that anybody is hurt in these accidents, but the reports seem surprisingly similar:

"Piper PA38-112 Tomahawk—. Nose gear collapsed on landing in gusty conditions at—."

"Piper PA38-112 Tomahawk—. Nose gear collapsed on landing at—"

"Piper PA38 Tomahawk—. Landing gear collapsed on landing at—Aerodrome probably due to pre-existing damage from an earlier unreported heavy landing"

The nosewheel is nowhere near as strong as the main undercarriage, but there is no need for its strength to be tested if a proper approach and landing technique is used. Approach speed for a normal approach with flap is about 70 knots, usually a little higher for a flapless approach; incorrect approach speed is a primary cause of 'ballooning', which often leads to bouncing. Bouncing also arises where the aircraft is allowed to touch down at too high a speed, usually in a level attitude rather than a nose up attitude. The correct action in either a 'balloon' or a bounce is to GO AROUND without delay. The correct landing technique is to approach at the proper speed, 'flare' or 'hold off', close the throttle, and gradually raise the nose to ensure a slow touch down speed on the MAINWHEELS FIRST, with the nose wheel still off the ground. With the effectiveness of the Tomahawk elevators this should be no problem. As the aircraft slows down correct use of the elevators means the nose wheel is allowed to gently contact the surface some time after the initial mainwheel contact. Again there is no substitute for flying instruction in the proper technique with a flying instructor.

The go-around in the Tomahawk does not provide any problems, even with full flap extended. The trim change when applying full power is manageable, and although the aircraft will climb with full flap extended, it is common practice to raise flaps to the 1st stage (21°) as part of the go-around procedure.

▶ Parking And Tie Down

The aircraft is generally parked into wind, it is good practice to stop with the nosewheel straight so that the rudder is not deflected. All switches should be off, and the doors closed. In extremely cold weather it may advisable NOT to set the parking brake as moisture may freeze the brakes, also the parking brake should not be set if there is reason to believe that the brakes are overheated. If for any reason the parking brake is not set the wheels should be 'chocked'.

When tying down the aircraft the following technique is recommended:

- ■ Park aircraft into wind with the flaps retracted.
- ■ Secure the flying control by looping the seat belt through the control wheel.
- ■ Tie ropes, cables or chains are attached to the wing tie down points and secured to ground anchor points.
- ■ If desired a rope (not cable or chain) can be secured to the nose leg and secured to a ground anchor point.
- ■ A rope can be passed through the tail tie down point and each end secured at 45° angle each side of the tail.
- ■ External control locks may be advisable in strong or gusty wind conditions.

It is also prudent to use a pitot cover, particularly if the aircraft will be left unattended for some time.

Good tie down can prevent wind damage!

Mixture and Carb Icing Supplement

Mixture and Carb Icing Supplement

▶ Carburettor Icing

▶ How Carburettor Icing Forms

▶ Conditions Likely to Lead to Carburettor Icing

▶ Carburettor Icing Conditions

▶ Symptoms of Carburettor Icing

▶ Use of Carburettor Heat

▶ The Mixture Control

▶ Reasons for Adjusting the Mixture

▶ Effect of Mixture Adjustment

▶ Use of the Mixture Control

▶ Carburettor Icing

Almost certainly the most common cause of engine rough running, and complete engine failures, is carburettor icing. Despite this carburettor icing remains a widely misunderstood subject, with many pilots' knowledge of the subject being limited to a feeling that the carb heat should be used regularly in flight, without really knowing the symptoms of carb. icing or the conditions most likely to cause its formation.

▶ How Carburettor Icing Forms

IMPACT ICING occurs when ice forms over the external air inlet (air filter) and inside the induction system leading to the carburettor. This type of icing occurs with the temperature below 0°C whilst flying in cloud, or in precipitation (ie rain, sleet or snow). These conditions are also conducive to airframe icing, and this aircraft is NOT CLEARED FOR FLIGHT INTO KNOWN ICING CONDITIONS, which clearly these are. So, assuming the aircraft is operated legally within its limitations, this form of icing should not occur, and is not considered further.

CARBURETTOR ICING is caused by a temperature drop inside the carburettor, which can happen even in conditions where other forms of icing will not occur. The causes of this temperature drop are twofold:

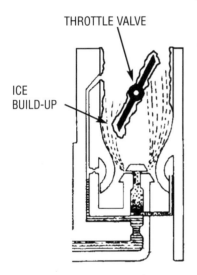

THROTTLE VALVE

ICE
BUILD-UP

1 FUEL ICING – the evaporation of fuel inside the carburettor. Liquid fuel changes to fuel vapour and mixes with the induction air causing a large temperature drop. If the temperature inside the carburettor falls below 0°C, water vapour in the atmosphere condenses into ice, usually on the walls of the carburettor passage adjacent to the fuel jet, and on the throttle valve. Generally fuel icing is responsible for around 70% of the temperature drop in the carburettor.

2 THROTTLE ICING – the temperature loss caused by the acceleration of air and consequent pressure drop around the throttle valve. This effect may again take the temperature below 0°C, and water vapour in the inlet air will condense into ice on the throttle valve. This practical effect is a demonstration of Bernoulli's Principle.

As fuel and throttle icing generally occur together, they are considered just as carburettor icing.

▶ Conditions Likely To Lead To Carburettor Icing

Two criteria govern the likelihood of carburettor icing conditions, the AIR TEMPERATURE and the RELATIVE HUMIDITY.

The ambient air temperature is important, BUT NOT BECAUSE THE TEMPERATURE NEEDS TO BE BELOW 0°C, OR EVEN CLOSE TO FREEZING. The temperature drop in the carburettor can be up to 30°C, so carburettor icing can (and does) occur in hot ambient conditions. No wonder carburettor icing is sometimes referred to as refrigeration icing. Carburettor icing is considered a possibility within the temperature range of -10°C to +30°C.

The relative humidity (a measure of the water content of the atmosphere) is the major factor. The greater the water content in the atmosphere (the higher the relative humidity), the greater the risk of carburettor icing. That said the relative humidity (RH) does not to have to be 100% (ie visible water droplets – cloud, rain), for carburettor icing to occur. Carburettor icing is considered a possibility at relative humidity values as low as 30%, but it is rare that the RH gets this low in Europe. Herein lies the real danger of carburettor icing, that it can occur in such a wide range of conditions. Obviously the pilot must be alert to the possibility of carburettor icing at just about all times. Flight in or near cloud, or in other visible moisture (ie rain) might be an obvious cause of carburettor icing, but – VISIBLE MOISTURE DOES NOT NEED TO BE PRESENT FOR CARBURETTOR ICING TO OCCUR.

▶Carburettor Icing Conditions

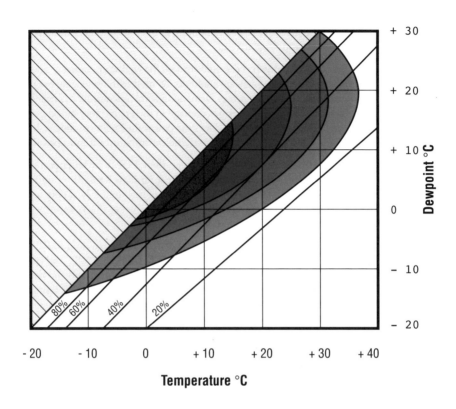

	100% Relative humidity
■	Serious icing – any power
■	Moderate icing – cruise power Serious icing – descent power
■	Serious icing – descent power
■	Light icing – cruise or descent power

▶Symptoms Of Carburettor Icing

In this aircraft, fitted with a fixed pitch propeller, the symptoms of carburettor icing are straightforward. A loss of RPM will be the first symptom, although this is often first noticed as a loss of altitude. As the icing becomes more serious, engine rough running may occur.

Carburettor icing is often detected during the use of the carburettor heat. Normally when the carburettor heat is used, a small drop in RPM occurs, when the control is returned to cold (off) the RPM restores to the same as before the use of carburettor heat. If the RPM restores to a higher figure than before the carburettor heat was used, it can be reasonably supposed that some form of carburettor icing was present.

▶Use Of Carburettor Heat

Apart from the normal check of carburettor heat during the power checks, it may be necessary to use the carburettor heat on the ground if carburettor icing is suspected. Safety considerations apart, the use of carburettor heat on the ground should be kept to a minimum, as the hot air inlet is unfiltered, and so sand or dust can enter the engine, increasing engine wear.

Carburettor icing is generally considered to be very unlikely with the engine operating at above 75% power, ie during the take-off and climb. Carburettor heat should not be used with the engine operating at above 75% power (ie full throttle) as detonation may occur. Detonation is the uncontrolled burning of fuel in the cylinders, literally an explosion, and will cause serious damage to the engine very quickly. Apart from the danger of detonation, the use of carburettor heat reduces the power the engine produces. In any situation where full power is required (ie take-off, climb, go-around) the carburettor heat must be off (cold).

Very few operators recommend the use of anything other than FULL carburettor heat. A normal carburettor icing check will involve leaving the carburettor heat on (hot) for 5-10 seconds, although the pilot may wish to vary this dependent on the conditions. The use of carburettor heat does increase the fuel consumption, and this may be a factor to consider if the aircraft is being flown towards the limit of its range/endurance in possible carburettor icing conditions.

With carburettor icing present, the use of carburettor heat may lead to a large drop in RPM, with rough running. The instinctive reaction is to put the carburettor heat back to cold (off), and quickly. This is, however, the wrong action. Chances are this rough running is a good thing, and the carburettor heat should be left on (hot) until the rough running clears and the RPM rises. In this instance the use of carburettor heat has melted a large amount of accumulated icing and the melted ice is passing through the engine, causing temporary rough running.

Carburettor heat control

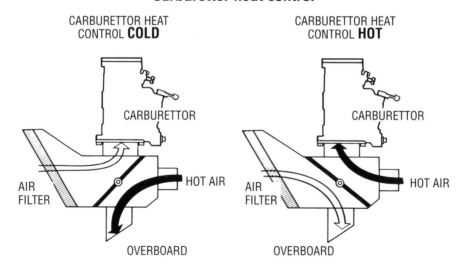

Care should be taken when flying in very cold ambient conditions (below -10°C). In these conditions the use of carburettor heat may actually raise the temperature in the carburettor to that most conducive to carburettor icing. Generally when the temperature in the carburettor is below -8°C moisture forms directly into ice crystals which pass through the engine.

The RPM loss normally associated with the use of carburettor heat is caused by the reduced density of the hot air entering the carburettor, leading to an over rich mixture entering the engine. If the carburettor heat has to be left constantly on (hot) – ie flight in heavy rain and cloud – it may be advisable to lean the mixture in order to maintain RPM and smooth engine running.

It is during the descent (and particularly the glide descent) that carburettor icing is most likely to occur. The position of the throttle valve (ie almost closed) is a contributory factor, and even though the carburettor heat is normally applied throughout a glide descent, the low engine power will reduce the temperature of the hot air selected with the carburettor heat control. In addition a loss of power may not be readily noticed. As the propeller is likely to windmill even after a complete loss of power and so a full loss of power may only be apparent when the throttle is opened at the bottom of the descent. This is one good reason for opening the throttle to 'warm the engine' at intervals during a glide descent.

▶The Mixture Control

The aircraft is provided with a mixture control so that the pilot can adjust the fuel/air mixture entering the engine. The cockpit mixture control operates a needle valve between the float bowl and the main metering jet. This valve controls the fuel flow to the main metering jet to adjust the mixture, with the mixture control in the ICO position (fully lean) the valve is fully closed.

▶Reasons For Adjusting The Mixture

Correct leaning of the engine mixture will enable the engine to be operated at its most efficient in terms of fuel consumption. With the increased use of 100LL fuel, leaning is also important to reduce spark plug fouling.

The most efficient engine operation is obtained with a fuel/air ratio of about 1:15, that is 1 part fuel to 15 parts air. In fact with the mixture set to fully rich, the system is designed to give a slightly richer mixture than ideal, typically about 1:12. This slightly over rich mixture reduces the possibility of pre-ignition or detonation, and aids cylinder cooling.

As altitude increases the air density decreases. Above about 3000' the reduced air density can lead to an over rich mixture. If the mixture becomes excessively rich, power will be lost, rough running may be evident and ultimately engine failure will occur due to a 'rich cut'. It is for this reason that the mixture control is provided to ensure the correct fuel/air ratio, typically it is used when cruising above 3000'.

The flight manuals for some older aircraft recommend leaning only above 5000'. However with the increasing use of AVGAS 100LL, and the plug fouling problems sometimes associated with 100LL, most operators recommend leaning once above 3000'.

▶Effect of Mixture Adjustment

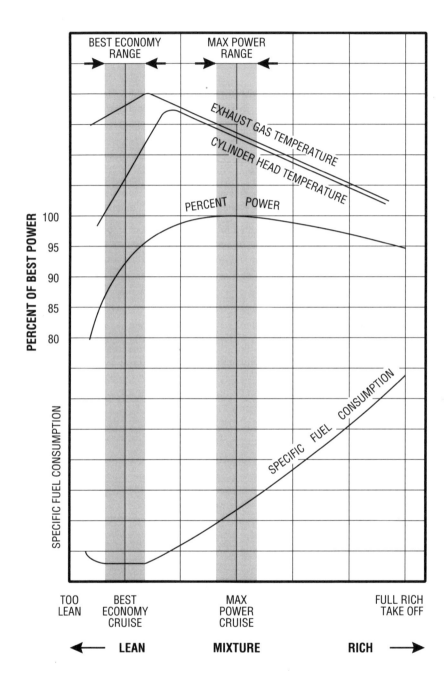

▶ Use Of The Mixture Control

For take-off and climb the mixture should be fully rich, the only exception being operation from a high density altitude airport when leaning may be necessary to ensure the availability of max. power. On reaching a cruising altitude above about 3000' the cruise power should be set, and then leaning can be carried out (note: generally leaning with over 75% power set is not recommended). If climbing above about 5000', full throttle will be less than 75% power on a normally aspirated engine and so leaning may be permissible to maintain smooth running.

Assuming that there is no Exhaust Gas Temperature (EGT) gauge and no cylinder head temperature gauge, the primary instrument to watch when leaning is the RPM gauge (tachometer).

To lean the engine, the recommended power setting (RPM) is set with the throttle. Next, with a constant throttle setting, the mixture control is slowly moved back (leaned). If leaning is required the RPM will increase slowly, peak, and then decrease as the mixture is leaned, if leaning is continued the engine will ultimately run rough and lose power.

If the mixture is set to achieve peak RPM, the maximum power mixture has been achieved.

If the mixture is set to give a tachometer reading 25-50RPM less than peak RPM on the 'lean' side, the best economy mixture has been achieved. This setting is the one that many aircraft manufacturers recommend (25-50RPM on the 'lean side' of peak RPM), and their performance claims are based on such a procedure.

Using a mixture that is too lean is a false economy, and will lead to serious engine damage sooner or later. Detonation (an uncontrolled explosive combustion of the mixture in the cylinder) is particularly dangerous, and can lead to an engine failure in a very short time. The use of a fully rich mixture during full power operations is specifically to ensure engine cooling and guard against detonation.

For any change in operating conditions (altitude, power setting) the mixture will need to be reset. It is particularly important that the mixture is set to fully rich before increasing the power setting.

During a descent from a high altitude, the mixture will gradually become too lean if not reset, leading to excessive cylinder temperatures, power loss and ultimately engine failure. Normally the mixture is set to fully rich prior to landing, unless operating at a high elevation airfield.

Moving the mixture to the fully lean position – ICO (Idle Cut Off) – closes the needle valve and so stops fuel supply to the main metering jet. This is the normal method for closing down the engine and ensures that no unburnt mixture is left in the engine.

NORMAL COMBUSTION   DETONATION

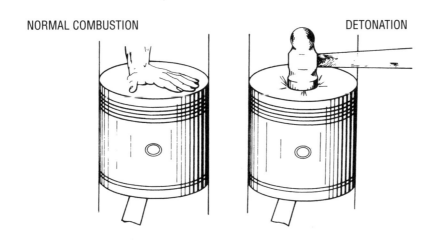

Expanded
Piper PA-38 Tomahawk
Pre-flight Checklist

Expanded Piper PA-38
Tomahawk Pre-flight Checklist

▶ Approaching Aircraft

▶ In Cabin

▶ Port Wing

▶ Port Undercarriage

▶ Front Fuselage and Engine

▶ Starboard Undercarriage

▶ Starboard Wing

▶ Starboard Fuselage

▶ Port Fuselage

▶Approaching Aircraft

Check for and remove any tie downs, external control locks, pitot cover and wheel chocks.

Look for any oil & fuel spillages from aircraft.

Remove any ice & frost from ALL surfaces.

Check for access to taxiways, obstructions, loose gravel etc.

Look to see if aircraft is on a level surface. A sloping surface will affect the visual check of fuel contents.

▶In Cabin

1   **Internal Control locks & Covers** ....Remove & Stow Securely

2   **Parking Brake** ....Check On with locking plate in

3   **Magneto Switches** ....Check OFF and Key Out

4   **Master Switch** ....On
    Turn on Pitot heater, anti-collision lights, landing light and
    navigation lights.
    Leave cockpit and check in turn :

5   **Stall Warner Vane** ....Move gently forward to check for klaxon operation

6   **Pitot Heat** ....Check with fingers that pitot head is warm (it may take a minute
    or so to warm up)

7   **Anti-Collision Lights** ....Check operation.
    Do not look directly at strobes whilst they are operating.

8   **Landing/Nav lights** ....Check
    For Navigation lights colours are :
    PORT (Left) – RED;
    STARBOARD (Right) – GREEN;
    REAR (Tail) – WHITE

Return to cockpit and turn off electrical services as in above

9   **Fuel** ....Turn On
    Check contents gauges

10 **Master Switch** ....Off

11 **Flaps** ....Lower to 1st Stage (21°)

12 **Trimmer** ....Check position neutral using indicator

13 **First Aid Kit** ....In Position, secure

14 **Fire Extinguisher** ....In Position,secure & serviceable
    (gauge at top should be in green arc)

▶External

Leave cockpit and begin at rear of wing. This should also be where you complete your checks.

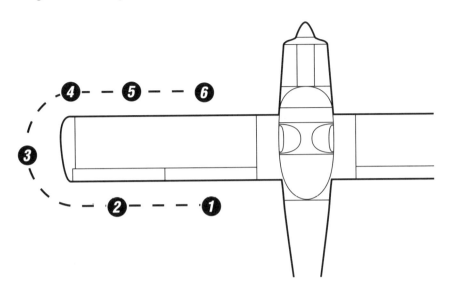

▶Port Wing

1 **Flap**...Upper and lower surface condition.
Particularly check inner lower surface for caked mud or stone damage from wheels.
Check linkages secure and greased

2 **Aileron**..Upper and lower surface condition, linkages & hinges secure, balance weight (next to wing tip) secure (with fingers inside hinge line hold the aileron with other hand – sudden down movement of aileron makes efficient cutting action!)
Check full and free movement
DO NOT USE FORCE

3 **Wing Tip** ....Condition,Security. Nav & Strobe Lights unbroken (This area is particularly vulnerable to hangar damage)

4 **Wing Surface**................................Upper & Lower surface condition.

5 **Wing Leading Edge** ....Check for dents along entire length Check stall warner vane movement gently – a click should be audible Check pitot head perforations unblocked
DO NOT BLOW INTO PITOT

6 **Fuel Tank** ....Check contents visually, resecure cap. Check fuel vent unblocked.
Take fuel drain sample from under tank if necessary – check for correct colour, water bubbles or sediment.
Check drain not leaking.

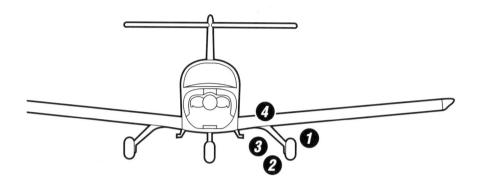

▶Port Undercarriage

1 **Tyre**..Check for tread & general condition.
                                        Check for correct inflation.
                                        Check alignment of creep marks.

2 **Hydraulic Lines**...........................Check for leaks (red fluid)

3 **Disc Brake**....................................Should be shiny, not rusty or pitted.

4 **Leg & Fairing**..............................Check condition especially fibreglass fairing. Look for mud or
                                        stone damage on wing & flap surface near undercarriage

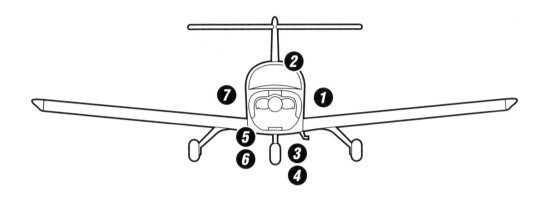

▶Front Fuselage & Engine

1   **Port Cowling** ....Open, check brake fluid level, and engine compartment generally (ie HT leads secure, oil leaks) Resecure cowling, take fuel sample if neccessary.
Check fuel drain not leaking.

2   **Windscreen**...................................Should be clean and insect free, OAT probe secure.

3   **Nose Leg** ....Oleo extension correct, linkages, nuts & split pins secure.

4   **Nose Wheel**..................................Check for tread & general condition.
Check for correct inflation.
Check alignment of creep marks.

5   **Front Cowling** ....Check condition & security. Intakes clear, Landing light unbroken.

6   **Propeller**......................................Look for cracks or chips especially leading edge.
Check spinner secure and condition good.
DO NOT MOVE OR SWING PROPELLER

7   **Starboard Cowling**......................Open engine compartment, check oil level, do NOT overtighten dipstick on resecuring.
Check engine compartment (ie HT leads secure etc).
Resecure cowling.

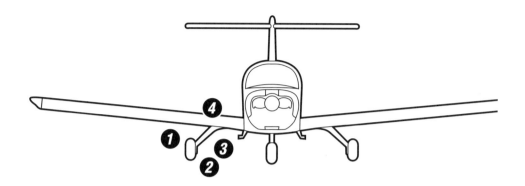

▶Starboard Undercarriage

1 **Tyre**..Check for tread & general condition.
Check for correct inflation. Look for alignment of creep marks.

2 **Hydraulic Lines**...........................Check for leaks (red fluid)

3 **Disc Brake** ....Should be shiny, not rusty or pitted.

4 **Leg & Fairing** ....Check condition especially fibreglass fairing. Look for mud or
stone damage on wing & flap surface near undercarriage

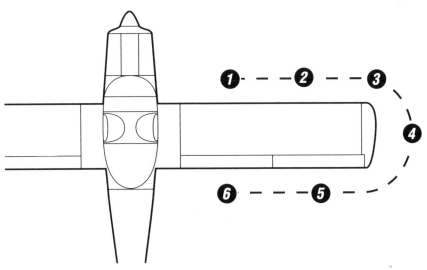

▶ Starboard Wing

1   **Fuel Tank**...................................Check contents visually, resecure cap.
Check fuel vent (under wing) unblocked. Take fuel drain sample if necessary.
Check drain not leaking.

2   **Wing Leading Edge**....................Check for dents along entire length.

3   **Wing Surface**...............................Upper & Lower surface condition

4   **Wing Tip**......................................Condition ,Security. Nav & Strobe Lights unbroken

5   **Aileron**...Upper and lower surface condition, linkages & hinges secure, balance weight (next to wing tip) secure. Remember to watch for aileron movement whilst checking inside hinge line
Check full and free movement gently
DO NOT USE FORCE

6   **Flap**...Upper and lower surface condition esp. near undercarriage.
Check linkages secure and greased.

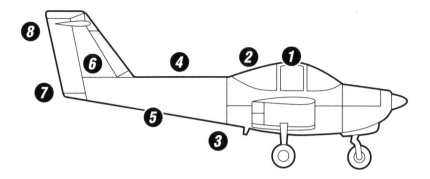

▶Starboard Fuselage

1   **Cockpit Door** ....Latch & Hinges secure

2   **Windows** ....Clean & uncracked

3   **Skin**...General surface condition upper and lower, look for wrinkles,
        dents or punctures

4   **Radio Aerials** ....Check secure

5   **Static Vent** ....Check clear & unblocked
        DO NOT BLOW INTO VENT

6   **Tail Fin**...Check skin condition,especially fairings;
        Check aerials secure.

7   **Rudder** ....Check condition, linkages secure & greased, nuts & split pins
        secure, Nav light unbroken.
        DO NOT ATTEMPT TO FORCE RUDDER MOVEMENT.

8   **Tailplane/Elevator**.......................Check condition, linkages secure
        Check other side of tail fin

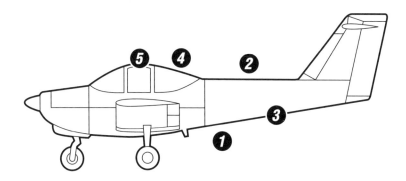

▶Port Fuselage

1   **Skin**..General surface condition, upper and lower, look for any
                                                    wrinkles, dents or punctures.

2   **Radio Aerials** ....Check secure

3   **Static Vent** ....Check clear & unblocked
                                                    DO NOT BLOW INTO VENT

4   **Windows** ....Check clean & uncracked

5   **Cockpit door** ....Check latches & hinges secure

IMPORTANT

REMEMBER: FULL REFERENCE MUST BE MADE TO AIRCRAFT FLIGHT MANUAL, PILOTS OPERATING HANDBOOK, AIPs, FLYING SCHOOL SYLLABUS/PILOTS ORDER BOOK, ETC

IF IN DOUBT – ASK

Loading and Performance

Loading and Performance

▶ Loading

▶ Mathematical Weight and Balance Calculation

▶ Use of the Loading Graph

▶ Performance

▶ Take-off Performance

▶ Take-off Distance Calculation Example

▶ Landing Performance

▶ Landing Distance Calculation Example

▶ Enroute Performance

▶ Runway Dimensions

▶ Loading

Aircraft loading can divided into two areas, the aircraft weight and the centre of gravity (c.g) position.

The aircraft must be loaded so that its weight is below the certified maximum take-off weight (1670lbs or 757 Kg). The weight limit is set primarily as a function of the lifting capability of the aircraft, which is largely determined by the wing design and engine power of the aircraft. Operating the aircraft when it is over weight will adversely effect the aircraft handling and performance, such as:

> Increased take-off speed and slower acceleration
>
> Increased runway length required for take-off
>
> Reduced rate of climb
>
> Reduced maximum altitude capability
>
> Reduced range and endurance
>
> Reduction in manoeuvrability and controllability
>
> Increased stall speed
>
> Increased approach and landing speed
>
> Increased runway length required for landing

The aircraft must also be loaded to ensure that its centre of gravity (c.g.) is within set limits, normally defined as a forward and aft limit in inches aft of the datum. For the Tomahawk the datum is the tip of the spinner. The forward limit is determined by the amount of elevator control available at landing speed, the aft limit is determined by the stability and controllability of the aircraft whilst manoeuvring. Attempted flight with the c.g. position outside of the set limits (either forward or aft) will lead to control difficulties, and quite possibly loss of control of the aircraft.

When loading the aircraft it is standard practice to calculate the weight and c.g. position of the aircraft at the same time, commonly known as the weight and balance calculation. Before going further it must be emphasised that the following examples are provided for illustrative purposes only. Each INDIVIDUAL aircraft has an INDIVIDUAL weight schedule that is valid only for that aircraft, and is dependent amongst other things on the equipment fitted to the aircraft. If the aircraft has any major modification, repair or new equipment fitted a new weight schedule will be produced. Therefore for any loading or performance calculations you must use the documents for the specific aircraft you will be using.

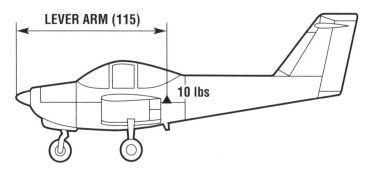

LEVER ARM (115) x WEIGHT (10) = MOMENT (1150)

As well as setting out limits the aircraft documents will also give lever arms for each item of loading. The lever arm is a distance from the aircraft datum. The weight multiplied by its lever arm gives its moment. Thus a set weight will have a greater moment the further away it is from the datum.

The operating weight of the aircraft can be split into three categories:

BASIC (EMPTY) WEIGHT – the weight of the aircraft, including unuseable fuel (and normally full oil). The weight and c.g. position of the aircraft in this condition will be noted in the weight schedule.

VARIABLE LOAD – weight of the crew (ie pilot). The weight schedule will give the lever arm for this load.

DISPOSABLE LOAD – weight of a passenger, fuel and baggage. Again the weight schedule will give a lever arm for each of these loads.

Firstly the pilot will need to calculate a weight for the variable and disposable load. It is obviously important to work in one set of units (either lbs or Kgs). This becomes more complicated for the fuel load where volume (litres, imperial gallons or U S gallons) will need to be converted into weight. This may be done in the weight schedule, but conversion tables are set out in the next section.

Weight And Centre Of Gravity Schedule

PRODUCED BY : **GROSVENOR AVIATION SERVICES (ENGINEERING) LIMITED**

AIRCRAFT TYPE: **PIPER PA38-112**

NATIONALITY AND
REGISTRATION MARKS: **G-BGRR**

CONSTRUCTOR'S SERIAL No: **78A0336**

MAXIMUM PERMISSIBLE WEIGHT: **1670lbs**

MAXIMUM LANDING WEIGHT: **1670lbs**

CENTRE OF GRAVITY LIMITS: **REFER TO FLIGHT MANUAL REP No. FAA 2126**

ALL LEVER ARMS ARE DISTANCES IN INCHES EITHER FORE OR AFT OF DATUM.

PART 'A' BASIC WEIGHT

The basic weight of this aircraft as calculated from Planeweighs Limited

Report No.1034 weighed on 08.07.88. at Manchester Airport is: **1182lbs**

The centre of gravity of aircraft in the same condition (aft of the datum) is: **74.66 ins.**

The total Moment about the datum in this condition in lb ins. is: **88254.45**

The DATUM referred to is defined in the Flight Manual, which is **66.25 ins.** forward of Wing leading edge.

The basic weight includes the weight of 12lbs unuseable fuel and 45lbs of oil and the weight of items indicated in Appendix 1 which comprises the list of basic equipment carried.

Each individual aircraft has an individual weight schedule, valid only for that aircraft. The weight schedule will state lever arms for each item of loading

▶ Mathematical Weight And Balance Calculation

With this method of calculation the weights of each item are listed together with their lever arm. Addition of all the weights is the first step, to ensure that the resulting figure is within the maximum permitted. Assuming this is the case the balance can then be calculated. For each item (except for the basic weight where the calculation is done already on the weight schedule) the weight is multiplied by the lever arm, to give a moment. Normally the lever arm is aft of the datum, to give a positive figure. If the lever arm quoted is forward of the datum the moment will be negative (although obviously the weight is NOT deducted from the weight calculation). All the moments are then added together, to give the total moment, and this figure is then divided by the total weight. The resulting figure will be the position of the c.g. , which can be checked to ensure it is within the set limits. The weight and c.g. position can be plotted on a graph in the flight manual. If the plotted position is within the 'envelope', the weight and c.g. position are within limits.

Example:

BASIC (EMPTY) WEIGHT: Aircraft G-BGRR
                            From the weight schedule from G-BGRR,
                            weight is 1182lbs

VARIABLE LOAD: Pilot 155lbs

DISPOSABLE LOAD: Passenger 140lbs
                            Rear Baggage 10lbs
                            Fuel Full (ie 30 US Gallons) 180lbs

You can simply add together the weights at this stage to check the all up weight, however it is more common to make up a table to check weight AND balance.

From the information above and on the weight schedule, we know the weight and lever arm for each item. The table is used to calculate the moment for each item (ie the weight x the lever arm).

Total weight, at 1667lbs is below the maximum permitted and so is acceptable.

ITEM	WEIGHT (lbs)	LEVER ARM	MOMENT
BASIC (EMPTY) WEIGHT – the weight, lever arm and moment are listed in the weight schedule			
G-BGRR	1182	74.66	88254.45
VARIABLE LOAD			
Pilot	155	85.5	13252.50
DISPOSABLE LOAD			
Passenger	140	85.5	11970.00
Rear Baggage	10	115.0	1150.00
Fuel	180	75.4	13572.00
TOTAL WEIGHT	1667	TOTAL MOMENT	128198.95

To find the Centre of Gravity position, the total moment is divided by the total weight:

$$\frac{128198.95}{1667} = 76.90 \text{ (inches aft of datum)}$$

This weight and centre of gravity position can now be plotted on the Weight and Centre of Gravity Envelope in the flight, manual to check if it is within limits:

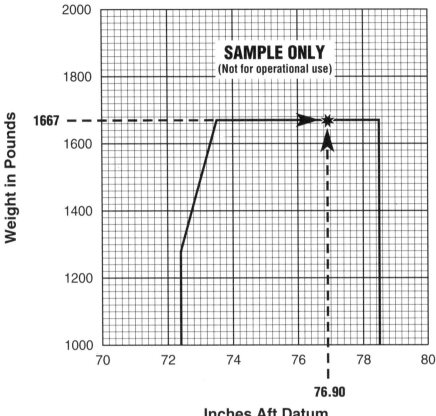

SAMPLE ONLY
(Not for operational use)

76.90

Inches Aft Datum

▶Use Of The Loading Graph

One problem with the mathematical calculation of weight and balance is the amount of maths involved (especially if you don't have a calculator handy !).

The loading graph can help here by cutting out the maths needed to calculate the moment. On the loading graph the mathematics of multiplying the weight by the lever arm are done for you (you don't even need to know the lever arm).

Using the same figures as before we can get the moments for the variable and disposable loads from the loading graph:

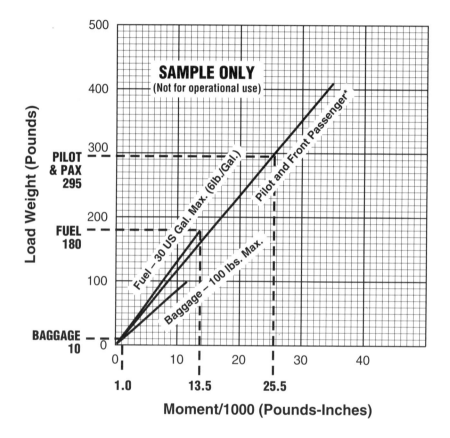

Now we can put these figures into a simplified table:

ITEM	WEIGHT	MOMENT/1000
G-BGRR	1182	88.25
Pilot & Passenger	295	25.50
Rear Baggage	10	1.00
Fuel	180	13.50
Total Weight = 1667	Total Moment/1000	= 128.25

At 1667lbs weight is within limits.

Again total moment (/1000) is divided by total weight (/1000):

$$\frac{128.25}{1.667} = 76.93 \text{ (inches aft of datum)}$$

Now the resulting C of G position is plotted on the Weight and Centre of Gravity Envelope to ensure the loading is with limits.

As you can see using the Loading Graph has resulted in a slightly different Centre of Gravity position, (as a result of the rounding up and down of the moments). As long as the result is still well within limits this is not a problem. If you get a result that is very close to the edge of the envelope it is worth using the mathematical method to get a more exact centre of gravity position.

A WORD OF WARNING. As well as the safety aspect, operating the aircraft outside its weight and balance envelope has far reaching legal and financial implications. Almost the first thing an accident investigator will check after an accident is the loading of the aircraft. If the loading is outside limits the pilot is contravening the Air Navigation Order. In addition both the aircraft insurance company and your personal insurance company will be unsympathetic when they know that the conditions of the Certificate of Airworthiness (ie the flight manual limitations) were not complied with. As the pilot in command the responsibility is yours alone.

▶ PA 38 Tomahawk Loading Graph

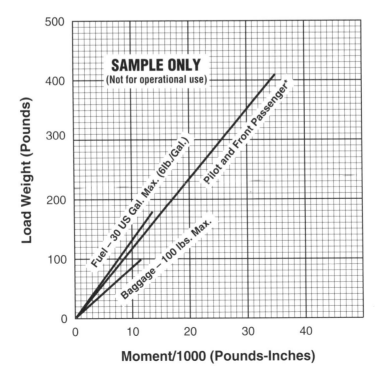

▶ PA 38 Tomahawk Weight and Centre of Gravity Envelope

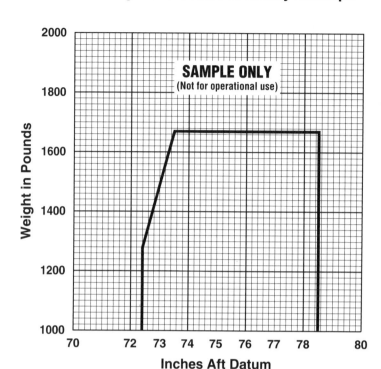

▶ Performance

The Tomahawk flight manual contains a section of graphs and tables to allow the pilot to calculate the expected performance of the aircraft for different flight phases. The most commonly used graphs are those for take-off and landing performance, and those are the ones we will concentrate on here. However the same principles can be used on the other graphs. Two things to remember: Firstly the chart performance is obtained by using the recommended techniques - to get graph results follow chart procedures. Secondly you can safely assume that the graph results have been obtained by placing a brand new aircraft in the hands of an experienced test pilot under favourable conditions.

To make allowances for a less than new aircraft, being flown by an average mortal in real conditions it is wise to 'factor' any results you get. Public transport operations are subject to overall factoring of 1.33 for take-offs and 1.43 for landings, this figure being incorporated in the relevant graphs. It is highly recommended that the pilot apply the same factor to any graph figures ie a calculated take-off distance of 500 metres becomes 500 x 1.33 = 665 metres. As with loading calculations the pilot must use the graphs and data from the documents for the individual aircraft being used. The graphs and diagrams used in this section are for illustrative purposes only, and not for operational use.

In the next section conversion factors between feet and metres are listed, together with recommended factors for variations not covered by the flight manual graphs.

▶ PA-38 Take-off and Landing Performance Graphs

The take-off distance and landing distance graphs in the flight manual make several assumptions (aircraft loaded to max gross weight; paved, level, dry, runway; use of flight manual technique). Different graphs may also be used for an aircraft with inboard AND outboard flow strips, or with only outboard flow strips. The graphs here assume an aircraft fitted with inboard AND outboard flow strips.

The graphs use the term "Pressure Altitude". This is the altitude of the runway assuming a standard pressure setting (ie 1013 mb - or 1013 hectopascal if you prefer). On a day with a QNH other than 1013 you will need to adjust the actual altitude to get the pressure altitude. For instance on a day with a QNH above 1013 the pressure altitude will be less than the actual, and vica versa. To do this conversion, simply adjust the actual altitude by 30ft for each millibar/hectopascal above or below 1013.

The headwind or tailwind component is calculated from the windspeed and the angle to the runway (ie a 10 knot wind directly down the runway gives a headwind component of 10 knots. A 10 knot wind at 90° to the runway gives a headwind component of 0). There is a graph in section 7 for calculating head/tail wind component and crosswind component.

The take-off distance & landing distance graphs will state the technique used to obtain the figures. Remember, to get graph results you have to use the graph techniques.

▶Take-off Performance

The take-off performance can be divided into two sections:

The TAKE-OFF RUN (or Take Off Ground Roll), the distance taken for the aircraft to become airborne, and;

The TAKE-OFF DISTANCE, that is the total distance required for the aircraft to become airborne AND clear a 50' barrier

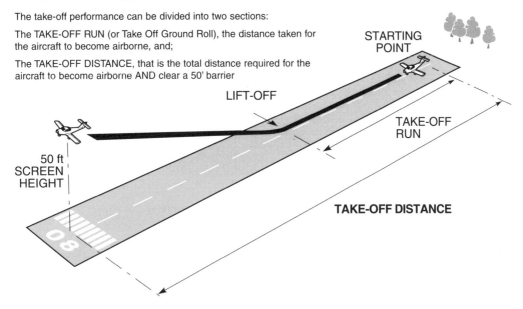

▶Take-off Distance Calculation Example

For this example we will take the conditions as:

Outside Air Temperature	+10°C
Pressure Altitude	1000ft
Headwind Component	10 Knots

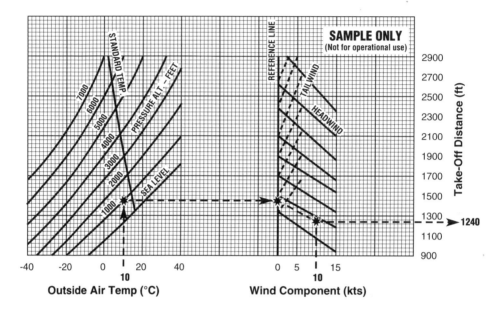

Start on the take-off distance graph at the temperature of +10°c, and then go vertically to the pressure altitude of 1000 feet. From this point go horizontally to the REFERENCE LINE, and THEN along the headwind guideline until above the 10 knots point. From this point take a line horizontally to the far side of the graph and read off the take-off distance in feet, – 1240ft. If this figure is factored by 1.33 you get the result of 1650ft.

▶Landing Performance

The landing performance is calculated as the LANDING DISTANCE, that is the total distance from 50' over the runway to a full stop. The ground roll (or ground run) – the distance from touch down to full stop may also be calculated

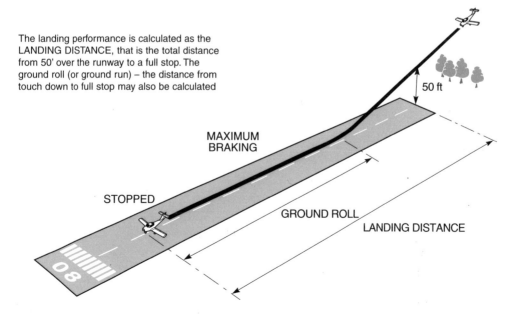

▶Landing Distance Calculation Example

For this example we will take the conditions as:

Outside Air Temperature	+20°C
Pressure Altitude	1000ft
Headwind Component	4 knots

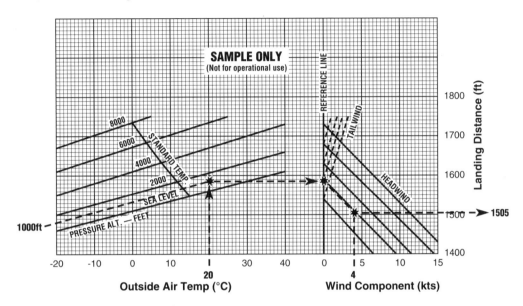

On the landing distance graph again start at the temperature (+20°c) and go vertically to the pressure altitude (1000ft). From this point go horizontally to the REFERENCE LINE, and then along the headwind guideline until above the headwind component (4 knots). From this point go horizontally to the far side of the graph and read off the landing distance in feet - 1505ft. If this figure is factored by 1.43 you get the result of 2152ft.

▶Enroute Performance

Data is also provided in the flight manual for calculating the enroute performance, such as range and endurance. It should be noted that the figures obtained in these charts rely on the use of the quoted procedures, particularly the leaning procedure. If any other procedure is used the quoted performance is unlikely to be achieved.

PA38 Take-Off Distance
Max Gross Weight, Paved Level Dry Runway

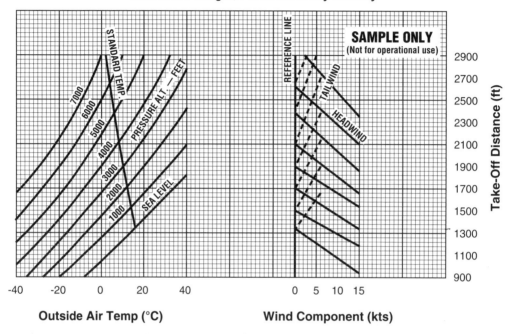

PA38 Landing Distance
Max Gross Weight, Paved Level Dry Runway

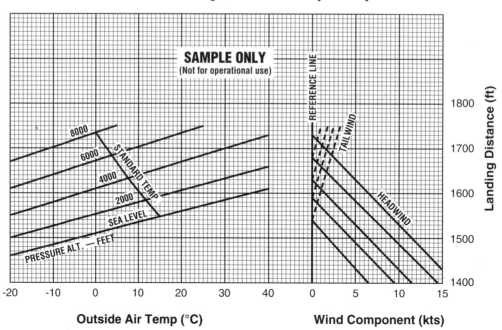

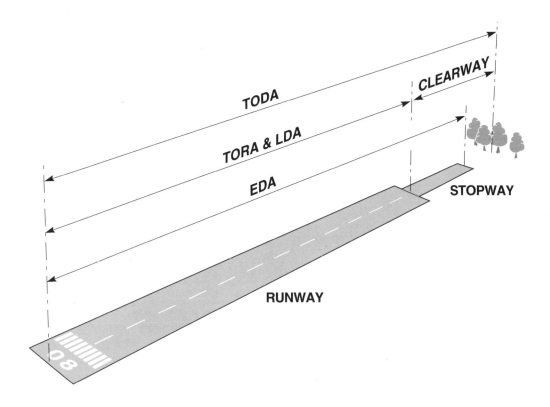

▶Runway Dimensions

Having calculated the distances the aircraft requires for take-off or landing, the runway dimensions must be checked to ensure that the aircraft can be safely operated on the runway in question. The figures given in the AIP or airfield guide can be defined in a number of ways.

The Take-off Run Available (TORA)

The TORA is the length of the runway available for the take-off ground run of the aircraft. This is usually the physical length of the runway.

The Emergency Distance Available (EDA)

The EDA is the length of the TORA plus the length of any stopway. A stopway is an area at the end of the TORA prepared for an aircraft to stop on in the event of an abandoned take-off. The ED is also known as the

ACCELERATE – STOP DISTANCE AVAILABLE.

The Take-off Distance Available (TODA)

The TODA is the TORA plus the length of any clearway. A clearway is an area over which an aircraft may make its initial climb (to 50' in this instance). The TODA will not be more than 1.5 x TORA.

The Landing Distance Available (LDA)

The LDA is the length of the runway available for the ground run of an aircraft landing. In all cases the landing distance required should never be greater than the landing distance available.

Conversions

Conversions

▶ Take-off Distance Factors

▶ Landing Distance Factors

▶ Runway Contamination

▶ Use of the Wind Component Graph

▶ Wind Component Graph

▶ Temperature and Pressure

▶ Distance – Metres/Feet

▶ Distance – Km/nm/sm

▶ Weight

▶ Volume – Fluid

▶ Millibars/Inches

▶Take-off Distance Factors

The following factors will allow the pilot to make allowance for variations that may affect take-off performance. Although some of these factors are covered in the PA 38 Tomahawk performance tables, the table is produced in its entirety for completeness:

VARIATION	INCREASE IN TAKE-OFF DISTANCE (to 50')	FACTOR
10% increase in aircraft weight	20%	1.2
Increase of 1000' in runway altitude	10%	1.1
Increase in temperature of 10°C	10%	1.1
Dry Grass		
– Short (under 5 inches)	20%	1.2
– Long (5-10 inches)	25%	1.25
Wet Grass		
– Short	25%	1.25
– Long	30%	1.3
2% uphill slope	10%	1.1
Tailwind component of 10% of lift off speed	20%	1.2
Soft ground or snow *	at least 25%	at least 1.25

* Snow and other runway contamination is covered on page 86.

▶ Landing Distance Factors

The following factors will allow the pilot to make allowance for variations that may affect landing performance. Although some of these factors are covered in the PA38 Tomahawk performance tables, the table is produced in its entirety for completeness:

VARIATION	INCREASE IN LANDING DISTANCE (from 50')	FACTOR
10% increase in aircraft weight	10%	1.1
Increase of 1000' in runway altitude	5%	1.05
Increase in temperature of 10°C	5%	1.05
Dry Grass		
– Short (under 5 inches)	20%	1.2
– Long (5-10 inches)	30%	1.3
Wet Grass		
– Short	30%	1.30
– Long	40%	1.40
2% downhill slope	10%	1.1
Tailwind component of 10% of landing speed	20%	1.2
Snow *	at least 25%	at least 1.25

* Snow and other runway contamination is covered on page 86.

▶ Runway Contamination

A runway can be contaminated by water, snow or slush. If operation on such a runway cannot be avoided additional allowance must be made for the problems such contamination may cause – ie additional drag, reduced braking performance (possible aquaplaning), and directional control problems.

It is generally recommended that take-off should not be attempted if dry snow covers the runway to a depth of more than 60mm, or if water, slush or wet snow covers the runway to more than 15mm. In addition a tailwind, or crosswind component exceeding 10 knots, should not be accepted when operating on a slippery runway.

For take-off distance required calculations the other known conditions should be factored, and the emergency distance available on the runway should be at least 2.0 x the take-off distance required (for a paved runway) or at least 2.66 x the take-off distance required (for a grass runway).

For landing any water or slush can have a very adverse effect on landing performance, and the danger of aquaplaning (with negligible wheel braking and loss of directional control) is very real.

▶Use of the Wind Component Graph

This graph can be used to find the head/tail wind component and the crosswind component, given a particular wind velocity and runway direction.

EXAMPLE:

Runway 27

Surface wind 240°/15 knots

The angle between the runway direction (270°) and wind direction(240°) is 30°. Now on the graph locate a point on the 30° line, where it crosses the 15 knot arc. From this point take a horizontal line to give the headwind component (13 knots) and a vertical line to give the crosswind component (8 knots).

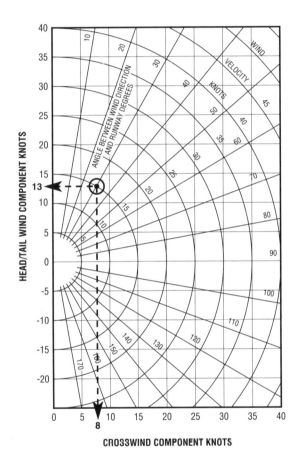

On the main graph overleaf the shaded area represents the maximum demonstrated crosswind component for this aircraft. If the wind point is within this shaded area, the maximum demonstrated crosswind component for this aircraft has been exceeded.

Note: Runway direction will be degrees magnetic. Check the wind direction given is also in degrees magnetic.

▶Wind Component Graph

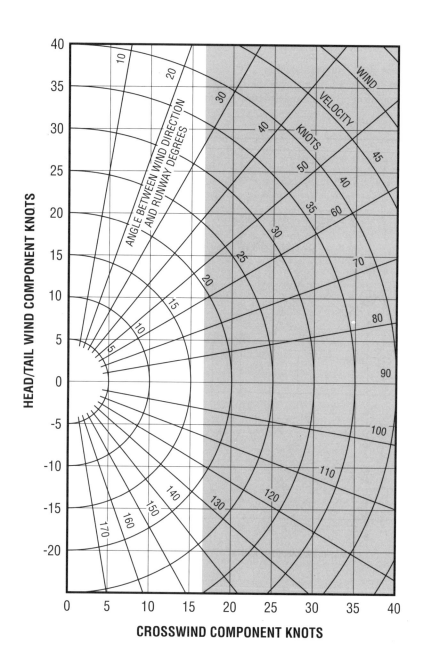

Temperature & Pressure

TEMPERATURE

°C: 50 40 30 20 10 0 −10 −20 −30 −40 −50 −60

°F: 120 110 100 90 80 70 60 50 40 30 20 10 0 −10 −20 −30 −40 −50 −60 −70

PRESSURE

kg/cm² : 7 6 5 4 3 2 1 0

lbs/sq" : 100 90 80 70 60 50 40 30 20 10 0

Bars: 7 6 5 4 3 2 1 0

Metric/Imperial Measurement

Metres	Feet	Feet	Metres
1	3.28	1	0.30
2	6.56	2	0.61
3	9.84	3	0.91
4	13.12	4	1.22
5	16.40	5	1.52
6	19.69	6	1.83
7	22.97	7	2.13
8	26.25	8	2.44
9	29.53	9	2.74
10	32.81	10	3.05
20	65.62	20	6.10
30	98.43	30	9.14
40	131.23	40	12.19
50	164.04	50	15.24
60	196.85	60	18.29
70	229.66	70	21.34
80	262.47	80	24.38
90	295.28	90	27.43
100	328.08	100	30.48
200	656.16	200	60.96
300	984.25	300	91.44
400	1,312.34	400	121.92
500	1,640.42	500	152.40
600	1,968.50	600	182.88
700	2,296.59	700	213.36
800	2,624.67	800	243.84
900	2,952.76	900	274.32
1000	3,280.84	1000	304.80
2000	6,561.70	2000	609.60
3000	9,842.50	3000	914.40
4000	13,123.40	4000	1,219.20
5000	16,404.20	5000	1,524.00
6000	19,685.00	6000	1,828.80
7000	22,965.90	7000	2,133.60
8000	26,246.70	8000	2,438.40
9000	29,527.60	9000	2,743.20
10000	32,808.40	10000	3,048.00

Conversion Factors:

Centimetres to Inches x .3937
Inches to Centimetres x 2.54
Metres to Feet x 3.28084
Feet to Metres x 0.3048

Km/Nautical Miles/Statute Miles

NM	Km	St	Km	NM	St
1	1.85	1.15	1	.54	.62
2	3.70	2.30	2	1.08	1.24
3	5.56	3.45	3	1.62	1.86
4	7.41	4.60	4	2.16	2.49
5	9.26	5.75	5	2.70	3.11
6	11.11	6.90	6	3.24	3.73
7	12.96	8.06	7	3.78	4.35
8	14.82	9.21	8	4.32	4.97
9	16.67	10.36	9	4.86	5.59
10	18.52	11.51	10	5.40	6.21
20	37.04	23.02	20	10.80	12.43
30	55.56	34.52	30	16.20	18.64
40	74.08	46.03	40	21.60	24.86
50	92.60	57.54	50	27.00	31.07
60	111.12	69.05	60	32.40	37.28
70	129.64	80.55	70	37.80	43.50
80	148.16	92.06	80	43.20	49.71
90	166.68	103.57	90	48.60	55.92
100	185.2	115.1	100	54.0	62.1
200	370.4	230.2	200	108.0	124.3
300	555.6	345.2	300	162.0	186.4
400	740.8	460.3	400	216.0	248.6
500	926.0	575.4	500	270.0	310.7
600	1111.2	690.5	600	324.0	372.8
700	1296.4	805.6	700	378.0	435.0
800	1481.6	920.6	800	432.0	497.1
900	1666.8	1035.7	900	486.0	559.2

Statute Miles to Nautical Miles x 0.868976
Statute Miles to Kilometres x 1.60934
Kilometres to Statute Miles x 0.62137
Kilometres to Nautical Miles x 0.539957
Nautical Miles to Statute Miles x 1.15078
Nautical Miles to Kilometres x 1.852

Volume (Fluid)

U.S Gall	Imp Gall	Litres	Imp Gall	U.S. Gall	Litres
1	0.83	3.79	1	1.20	4.55
2	1.67	7.57	2	2.40	9.09
3	2.50	11.36	3	3.60	13.64
4	3.33	15.14	4	4.80	18.18
5	4.16	18.93	5	6.00	22.73
6	5.00	22.71	6	7.21	27.28
7	5.83	26.50	7	8.41	31.82
8	6.66	30.28	8	9.61	36.37
9	7.49	34.07	9	10.81	40.91
10	8.33	37.85	10	12.01	45.46
20	16.65	75.71	20	24.02	90.92
30	24.98	113.56	30	36.03	136.38
40	33.31	151.41	40	48.04	181.84
50	41.63	189.27	50	60.05	227.30
60	49.96	227.12	60	72.06	272.76
70	58.29	264.97	70	84.07	318.22
80	66.61	302.82	80	96.08	363.68
90	74.94	340.68	90	108.09	409.14
100	83.27	378.54	100	120.09	454.60

Litres	Imp Gall	U.S. Gall
1	0.22	0.26
2	0.44	0.53
3	0.66	0.79
4	0.88	1.06
5	1.10	1.32
6	1.32	1.59
7	1.54	1.85
8	1.76	2.11
9	1.98	2.38
10	2.20	2.64
20	4.40	5.28
30	6.60	7.93
40	8.80	10.57
50	11.00	13.21
60	13.20	15.85
70	15.40	18.49
80	17.60	21.14
90	19.80	23.78
100	22.00	26.42
200	44.00	52.84
300	66.00	79.26
400	88.00	105.68
500	110.00	132.10
600	132.00	158.52
700	154.00	184.94
800	176.00	211.36
900	198.00	237.78
1000	220.00	264.20

Conversion Factors:
Imperial Gallons to Litres x 4.54596
Litres to Imperial Gallons x 0.219975
U.S. Gallons to Litres x 3.78541
Litres to U.S. Gallons x 0.264179
Imperial Gallons to U.S. Gallons x 1.20095
U.S. Gallons to Imperial Gallons x 0.832674

Weight lbs/Kg

lbs	Kg	Kg	lbs
1	.45	1	2.20
2	.91	2	4.41
3	1.38	3	6.61
4	1.81	4	8.82
5	2.27	5	11.02
6	2.72	6	13.23
7	3.18	7	15.43
8	3.63	8	17.64
9	4.08	9	19.84
10	4.54	10	22.05
20	9.07	20	44.09
30	13.61	30	66.14
40	18.14	40	88.18
50	22.68	50	110.23
60	27.22	60	132.28
70	31.75	70	154.32
80	36.29	80	176.37
90	40.82	90	198.42
100	45.4	100	220.5
200	90.7	200	440.9
300	136.1	300	661.4
400	181.4	400	881.8
500	226.8	500	1102.3
600	272.2	600	1322.8
700	317.5	700	1543.2
800	362.9	800	1763.7
900	408.2	900	1984.2
1000	453.6	1000	2204.6
2000	907.2	2000	4409.2
3000	1360.8	3000	6613.9
4000	1814.4	4000	8818.5
5000	2268.0	5000	11023.1
6000	2721.5	6000	13227.7
7000	3175.1	7000	15432.3
8000	3628.7	8000	17637.0
9000	4082.3	9000	19841.6
10000	4535.9	10000	22046.2

Km/Nautical Miles/Statute Miles

ST	NM	Km
1	.87	1.61
2	1.74	3.22
3	2.61	4.83
4	3.48	6.44
5	4.34	8.05
6	5.21	9.66
7	6.08	11.27
8	6.95	12.87
9	7.82	14.48
10	8.69	16.09
20	17.38	32.19
30	26.07	48.28
40	34.76	64.37
50	43.45	80.47
60	52.14	96.56
70	60.83	112.65
80	69.52	128.75
90	78.21	144.84
100	86.9	161.0
200	173.8	321.9
300	260.7	482.8
400	347.6	643.7
500	434.5	804.7
600	521.4	965.6
700	608.3	1126.5
800	695.2	1287.5
900	782.1	1448.4

Conversion Factors:
lbs to Kilograms x 0.45359
Kilograms to lbs x 2.20462

Millibars/Inches

Mbs	ins	Mbs	ins	Mbs	ins	Mbs	ins
950	28.054	980	28.939	1010	29.825	1040	30.711
951	28.083	981	28.969	1011	29.855	1041	30.741
952	28.113	982	28.998	1012	29.884	1042	30.770
953	28.142	983	29.028	1013	29.914	1043	30.800
954	28.172	984	29.058	1014	29.943	1044	30.829
955	28.201	985	29.087	1015	29.973	1045	30.859
956	28.231	986	29.117	1016	30.002	1046	30.888
957	28.260	987	29.146	1017	30.032	1047	30.918
958	28.290	988	29.176	1018	30.062	1048	30.947
959	28.319	989	29.205	1019	30.091	1049	30.977
960	28.349	990	29.235	1020	30.121	1050	31.007
961	28.378	991	29.264	1021	30.150		
962	28.408	992	29.294	1022	30.180		
963	28.437	993	29.323	1023	30.209		
964	28.467	994	29.353	1024	30.239		
965	28.496	995	29.382	1025	30.268		
966	28.526	996	29.412	1026	30.298		
967	28.556	997	29.441	1027	30.327		
968	28.585	998	29.471	1028	30.357		
969	28.615	999	29.500	1029	30.386		
970	28.644	1000	29.530	1030	30.416		
971	28.674	1001	29.560	1031	30.445		
972	28.703	1002	29.589	1032	30.475		
973	28.733	1003	29.619	1033	30.504		
974	28.762	1004	29.648	1034	30.534		
975	28.792	1005	29.678	1035	30.564		
976	28.821	1006	29.707	1036	30.593		
977	28.851	1007	29.737	1037	30.623		
978	28.880	1008	29.766	1038	30.652		
979	28.910	1009	29.796	1039	30.682		

To convert Inches into millibars multiply by 33.86
To convert millibars into Inches multiply by 0.0295

Index

Index